The Ultimate Case Interview Workbook:

Exclusive Cases and Problems for Interviews at Top Consulting Firms

Taylor Warfield

Copyright © 2020 by Taylor Warfield

ISBN-13: 978-1-7333381-0-3

Table of Contents

Introduction

Consulting is a very competitive field to get into. Each year, tens of thousands of candidates from top undergraduate and MBA programs will submit their resume in hopes of landing a career-shaping job in consulting. Among those, a small pool will be invited to interview for the job. Among those that interview, a select group will receive consulting job offers. What separates candidates that land a consulting job offer from those that don't?

Once you have a consulting interview, it all comes down to how well you perform during that interview. Besides getting asked typical behavioral questions, such as "tell me about a time when you led a group," and personal questions, such as "why do you want to work at this firm?", you'll inevitably get a case interview or "case."

There is no way to avoid these case interviews. You will definitely be given one. In a first-round interview, you can expect 1-2 cases. In the final round, expect 2-4 cases. In total, you're looking at 3-6 cases that you absolutely need to crush in order to get a consulting offer. Messing up in just one case interview can be the difference between receiving a consulting job offer and not receiving one. It is imperative that you are fully prepared for these case interviews.

What is a case interview?

Case interviews are the primary way that top consulting firms, such as McKinsey, BCG, Bain, Oliver Wyman, and Accenture, select candidates. In a case interview, an interviewer may ask a relatively broad business problem such as:

1

- An airline company is experiencing declining profits, what is causing this and what should they do about it?

- A boutique brick and mortar clothes retailer is looking into expanding into an international market. Which country should they look into entering first?

- Should a private equity firm purchase a roofing tile distributor?

- How do we price a new drug that treats multiple sclerosis, an autoimmune disease?

- Where can we achieve operational improvements for oil drilling in an energy utility company?

In a standard case interview, you will work closely with your interviewer for between 30 minutes to one hour. You will develop a framework to tackle these complex problems and then focus on a few key areas to investigate.

Your interviewer may provide you with data in the form of tables, charts, and graphs. Your interviewer may also ask you to estimate the size of a particular market, forcing you to make up assumptions and numbers along the way. They could also ask for your business judgment on an open-ended, qualitative question. At the end of the case, the interviewer will ask you for your recommendation for what the company should do to address their problem.

Case interviews can be quite varied and diverse. They can cover any industry, from consumer packaged goods to financial services to pharmaceuticals. They can cover any functional topic, from profitability to new market entry to mergers and acquisitions. Case interviews can be challenging, but they are an effective way for consulting companies to identify strong potential employees.

What are interviewers looking for and how can I do well in a case interview?

In just 30 minutes to one hour, case interviews can test for multiple different skills and competencies. This is why they are so widely used for consulting interviews. There are five main qualities that interviewers are looking for.

First, interviewers are looking for logical, structured thinking. Can you structure complex problems in a clear, simple way? Can you take tremendous amounts of information and boil it down to the most important points? Can you use logic and reason to make appropriate conclusions?

Second, interviewers are looking for analytical problem solving. Besides being able to perform math calculations quickly and easily, are you comfortable looking at data and finding the golden nuggets of insights? Can you set up and solve equations to determine financial implications?

Third, interviewers are testing for your general business acumen. Do your conclusions and recommendations make sense from a business perspective? Do you have a basic understanding of business concepts, such as profit, market share, and competitive advantage?

Fourth, interviewers are looking at your communication skills. Can you communicate in a clear, concise way? Are you easy to understand and follow?

Finally, interviewers are looking for personality and cultural fit. Consulting firms want to see if you are coachable, easy to work with, and pleasant to be around.

As you can see, there are many different skills and competencies that interviewers look for. Very few people can walk into a case interview unprepared and succeed. For the vast majority, doing well in a case interview requires serious practice.

Relentless practice and repetition lead to mastery of case interviews. There is no substitute for this. Once you know what a case interview is and what approaches and strategies to use, you will spend most of your time practicing.

What is the purpose of this book?

The goal of this book is to provide high-quality practice problems and full-length practice cases to help you hone your case interview skills. Instead of providing hundreds of repetitive practice problems, we have specifically written each practice problem and practice case to teach you something new. We want to maximize your learning and help you become an expert at solving case interviews as fast as possible. By the end of this book, you should feel much more confident and prepared for when your interview day comes.

This book is meant to supplement your existing knowledge of case interviews by providing essential practice problems and challenging practice cases. If you don't have an approach or strategy for tackling case interviews and consider yourself new to case interviews, I would recommend checking out my other resources. While this book will briefly summarize strategies for tackling each part of the case interview, my other resources will cover these strategies in more detail.

What other resources should I use if I want to learn case interviews as quickly as possible?

If you need an introduction to case interviews, I recommend reading Hacking the Case Interview. This book provides a concise overview of what you need to do and say in every single step of a case interview. This includes strategies on: crafting unique and tailored frameworks for every case scenario, handling quantitative problems, and answering qualitative questions. The book also provides a review of essential business concepts and principles.

For those looking for a one-week crash course on consulting case interviews, use the online course at **HackingTheCaseInterview.com**. The goal of the crash course is to help you pass your upcoming interview in the shortest amount of time possible. It is an all-inclusive course that contains (1) all of the strategies and knowledge you need to know, and (2) all of the practice problems and cases you need to do to quickly become a case interview expert.

Through this online crash course:

- Engage with 50+ concise video lessons that consolidate hundreds of hours of knowledge and experience into a 10-15 hour learning experience

- Learn advanced strategies to differentiate yourself from other candidates and become a top 1% interview candidate

- Hone your case interview skills through 15 additional challenging practice cases

Who am I?

By the time I had finished interviewing with consulting firms, I had done and given 200+ practice cases and had interviewed at over ten different firms. My hard work paid off, as I received multiple offers and ended up signing with Bain & Company.

In my first few years of work, I led case interview workshops across schools in the US and gave many case interviews to candidates. I also worked with high-potential candidates and helped many of them receive multiple job offers.

This book is a compilation of all of the hundreds of hours of case interview experience I have accumulated. I hope that this book will help you receive your dream job offer.

The firs
the begi

•

•

How to Best Use th

This book is divided into two sections: (1)
full-length practice cases.

In the first section, we'll visit all of the di
you could get asked in a case interview
questions include:

- Framework questions

- Market sizing & estimation question

- Profitability questions

- Interpreting charts & graphs

- Brainstorming questions

- Business judgment questions

For each type of question, we'll briefly descri
for how to approach the problem, provid
problems, and then provide detailed answers

The goal of the first section is to dive deep
interview question and thoroughly practice e
achieve mastery. If there is a particular type o
especially weak in, I recommend that you
section to work on getting better at it. Else, yo
practice problems in any order that you like.

Answe
but kno
solving

Once y
individ
second

The go
intervi
everyth
and so

Unless
differe
recom
the fir
come

When
recom
This
Howe
writte
indivi

With

section also includes questions that you may get asked at
ning or end of an interview:

Why consulting?" & "why this firm?" questions

ehavioral questions

ng these questions well is just as important as solving cases,
w that 80% of your interview time will typically be spent
case interviews.

ou have built confidence and expertise solving all of the
al different types of questions in a case interview, the
section of the book provides full-length practice cases.

l of the second section is to simulate a real, full-length case
w as closely as possible. In this section, you can put
ing you've learned and practiced in the first section together
ve cases holistically.

you feel confident in your abilities answering all of the
t types of questions you could get asked in an interview, I
end saving these full-length practice cases until you finish
section of the book. High-quality practice cases are hard to
y and this way, you won't be "wasting" the practice cases.

working through these full-length practice cases, I
end doing them with a case interview partner if possible.
ay, you better simulate what a real case interview is like.
er, given that this is not possible for everyone to do, I have
the practice cases such that you can complete them
ually if needed.

ll of that said, let's get started!

Part I: Practice Problems

Framework Questions

When you are initially given the case background information, you will first need to develop a framework to tackle the business problem. A framework is a tool you use to structure and break down a complex business problem into smaller, simpler components. It is a tool that will help you develop and support a recommendation.

A framework structures and presents the ideas and thoughts we have in our head in a clear and easy to understand way. In addition, it outlines the important areas we need to investigate and what major questions we need to answer in order to have a supported recommendation.

Remember that there is no single correct framework to use. For a given case, every candidate will likely have and use a different framework. However, not all frameworks are created equally.

Outstanding frameworks are structured, relevant, clear, and complete. Poor frameworks are not well structured, contain irrelevant elements, are confusing, and are missing key elements that are imperative to solving the case.

For this reason, I recommend that candidates do not use pre-memorized frameworks for solving cases. When you force yourself to use a memorized framework for an individual case, there is a high likelihood that your framework will contain elements not relevant to the case. When creating a framework, you should always be thinking critically for yourself to identify the most relevant elements of the case instead of regurgitating memorized information thoughtlessly.

The general framework strategy I recommend to candidates is to memorize 8-10 robust, versatile elements. Examples of good elements to use include: market attractiveness, customer needs, competitive landscape, company capabilities, profitability, risks, and strategic alternatives.

During the case, when it is time to develop a framework, ask for a few minutes to collect and structure your thoughts. During the 3-4 minutes of silence, mentally run through the 8-10 elements that you have already memorized and select the most relevant ones. An outstanding, complete framework typically has 3-5 different elements.

If running through this mental list of elements does not give you the 3-5 elements needed, think of and create your own elements that are specifically relevant to the case. Afterward, once we have our 3-5 different elements, we'll add sub-bullets to the elements to add more detail to our framework.

Remember that this framework strategy is meant to be robust and flexible. So, tailor your elements names to the case and create your own element if necessary.

In this book, we'll present frameworks in the following format:

- Element #1
  - Sub-bullet
  - Sub-bullet

- Element #2
  - Sub-bullet
  - Sub-bullet

- Element #3
  - Sub-bullet
  - Sub-bullet

- Element #4
    - Sub-bullet
    - Sub-bullet

Creating a framework for the case is by far the most difficult and stressful part of the case interview. Therefore, make sure to practice creating unique and tailored frameworks to a variety of different case situations. Again, don't rely on using memorized frameworks. That strategy will not work most of the time and interviewers can tell when you are using a memorized framework.

Case framework problem #1: Pineapple Co. is a large producer of non-organic pineapples in the US. They are considering producing organic pineapples that are grown without the use of pesticides in order to enter the premium, organic fruit market. Should they enter the organic pineapple market?

Solution to #1: This is a standard market entry case that is very common in first round interviews. Make sure you know this type of case very well. The key questions you want to know are:

- Is the organic pineapple market attractive?

- Can Pineapple Co. capture meaningful market share?

- Does Pineapple Co. have the capabilities to enter?

- Will Pineapple Co. be profitable after entering?

Building upon these key questions, one potential framework may look like the following:

- Organic pineapple market attractiveness
    - What is the market size?
    - What is the market growth rate?
    - What are average profit margins in the market?

- Organic pineapple competitive landscape
    - How many competitors are in the organic pineapple market?

- How much share does each competitor have?
- Do competitors have any competitive advantages or differentiation?

- Pineapple Co. capabilities
  - Does Pineapple Co. have the expertise to grow organic pineapples?
  - Does Pineapple Co. have the distribution channels to sell these organic pineapples?

- Expected profitability
  - What will the expected revenues be?
  - What will the expected costs be?
  - How long will it take to break even from entering this market?

Notice that each main bullet in this framework answers one of the four key questions we initially identified.

- Whether the market is attractive is addressed by "Organic pineapple market attractiveness"

- Whether Pineapple Co. can capture meaningful market share is addressed by "Organic pineapple competitive landscape"

- Whether Pineapple Co. actually has the capability to enter is addressed by "Pineapple Co. capabilities"

- Whether Pineapple Co. will be profitable after entering is addressed by "Expected profitability"

Also, note the logical sequence of each of the main bullets. We first determine if the market is attractive. Then, we determine if the market is easy or difficult to enter. Next, we determine if Pineapple Co. has the capabilities to enter. Finally, we determine if Pineapple Co. will be profitable if they enter the market.

In this framework, the sub-bullets support each framework element. For example, let's take a look at the first framework element,

"Organic pineapple market attractiveness." By knowing the market size, growth rate, and average profit margins, we will be able to determine whether the organic pineapple market is attractive. This same logical structure holds for all of the other framework elements.

Case framework problem #2: An electric car manufacturer has recently been experiencing a decline in profits. What is causing this decline in profits and what should they do to address this?

Solution to #2: This is a standard profit case that is very common in first round interviews. Make sure you know this type of case very well. Market entry and profit cases are the two most common types of cases you'll see in first round interviews. They are a quick and easy way for the interviewer to assess your capabilities to solve basic cases.

To answer this problem, we need to think about the decline in profits from both a quantitative and qualitative perspective.

We want to know quantitatively, what driver is causing the decline? In other words, is the decline in profits driven by a decline in revenue or an increase in costs, or both?

Next, we want to know qualitatively, why is this happening? We can look at factors such as changes among customers, changes among markets, or changes happening in the market overall.

From this, we'll know both what is responsible for the decline in profits and why it is happening.

- Drivers of profit
  - Has there been a decline in revenue?
    - Have sales gone down?
    - Have prices gone down?
  - Has there been an increase in costs?
    - Have variable costs increased?
    - Have fixed costs increased?

- Customer needs and preferences
  - Have customer needs changed?

- o Have customers changed their purchasing habits?
- o Do customers view our company differently?

- Competitors
  - o Have new competitors entered the market?
  - o Have existing competitors made any recent strategic moves or changes?

- Electric car market trends
  - o Are there new technologies impacting the market?
  - o Are there new regulations impacting the market?

For these cases, you'll typically want to start digging into the "Drivers of profit" first. Once you have determined the driver causing the decline in profits, you'll then want to dig into understanding, qualitatively, why this decline is happening. Afterward, you'll brainstorm and develop recommendations to address the decline in profits.

Case framework problem #3: Gaming Co. has three casinos situated in Atlantic City. One of their competitors, Lucky Fun Casinos, recently opened up a new casino in the area. How should Gaming Co. react to the opening of this new casino?

Solution to #3: When thinking about creating a framework for this case, it's useful to first determine just how threatening this new casino will be. Next, it will be important to determine how both customers and competitors will respond to this new casino opening. Finally, once we have collected all of this information, we can enumerate Gaming Co.'s strategic options and decide which one makes the most sense based on the information gathered so far.

One potential framework could look like the following:

- New casino threat size
  - o How large is this new casino?
  - o How close is this new casino to one of Gaming Co.'s casinos?
  - o Does this new casino have any differentiation or competitive advantages?

16

- Customer response
  - How will customers perceive and react to this new casino?
  - How likely are Gaming Co.'s customers to switch to this new casino?

- Competitor response
  - Will competitors also open a new casino?
  - Will competitors close their existing casinos?
  - What else would competitors do?

- Gaming Co. strategic options
  - Should Gaming Co. do nothing?
  - Should Gaming Co. open a new casino?
  - Should Gaming Co. close their existing casino?
  - Should Gaming Co. improve their existing casinos?
  - Should Gaming Co. do something else?

Case framework problem #4: JJR is a global private equity firm with over $100B in assets under management. They are considering purchasing a roofing tile supplier. Should they make this investment?

Solution to #4: For most private equity cases, you are most likely looking for an attractive, successful company to acquire. The private equity firm will then grow that company and sell that company later at a higher price to achieve a specific level of return on investment.

It is rare that you will get a case in which a private equity firm is looking to acquire a poorly performing company to turn around and then resell at a higher price. Nevertheless, it is best practice to confirm with the interviewer what exactly the private equity firm's acquisition strategy is.

For this problem, we'll assume that the private equity firm is looking to acquire an attractive, successful company. Therefore, one potential framework could look like the following:

- Roofing tile market attractiveness
    - What is the market size?
    - What is the market growth rate?
    - What are average profit margins for this market?

- Roofing tile competitive landscape
    - How many roofing tile suppliers are there?
    - How much share does each supplier have?
    - Do other players have any competitive advantages or differentiation?

- Acquisition target attractiveness
    - Is the acquisition target profitable?
    - How much market share does the target have?
    - Does the acquisition target have any differentiation or competitive advantages?

- Financial considerations
    - Is the acquisition price fair and reasonable?
    - By how much will JJR be able to improve and grow the acquisition target?
    - What is the expected return on this acquisition?

Case framework problem #5: Saver Technologies has developed proprietary software with artificial intelligence and machine learning that enables business owners to complete and file their annual taxes in under an hour. Typically, this task takes business owners a week to complete. How much should Saver Technologies price this product for?

Solution to #5: Remember that for pricing cases, there are generally three different strategies to price a product or service. You can price something according to the economic value or utility that it provides customers. You can also price something according to what competitors are pricing a similar product or service for. Finally, you can price something according to the costs to produce that product and then add on a certain profit margin to the price.

One potential framework could look like the following:

- Price by profit margin
  - o How much did it cost to produce this proprietary software?
  - o How much does it cost to acquire a customer?
  - o How much does it cost to supply a customer with this software?
  - o What profit margin is Saver Technologies hoping to achieve?

- Price by comparing competitor prices
  - o How much do competitors price their tax software products for?
  - o How do competitor tax software products perform compared to Saver Technologies' product?

- Price by customer willingness to pay
  - o How much time does this product save customers?
  - o How much do customers value that time for?

Remember that for pricing cases, you may end up combining several of these strategies. The cost to produce this proprietary software may set the lowest price Saver Technologies would be willing to sell the product for. Calculating the economic value or utility this product provides customers may set the maximum price customers are willing to pay. You may need to investigate competitor prices to determine where in this spectrum of prices is the sweet spot to price this product.

Case framework problem #6: Entertainment Co. produces 3-4 blockbuster movies every year. They focus on producing superhero movies, filming and shooting famous actors in live action. They are considering purchasing an animation studio, Bixar, which would help them produce animated movies. Should they make this acquisition?

Solution to #6: There can be quite a bit of overlap in the frameworks between private equity acquisition cases and corporate acquisition cases. For corporate acquisition cases, it is more important to consider potential synergies. Here is what one potential framework could look like:

- Animated movies market attractiveness
  - o What is the market size?
  - o What is the market growth rate?
  - o What are average profit margins for this market?

- Bixar company attractiveness
  - o Is Bixar profitable?
  - o How much market share does Bixar have?
  - o Does Bixar have any differentiation or competitive advantages?

- Synergies
  - o Are there potential revenue synergies that could exist between Entertainment Co. and Bixar?
  - o Are there potential cost synergies?

- Financial considerations
  - o Is the acquisition price fair and reasonable?
  - o How long will it take to break even on this acquisition?

Case framework problem #7: Garbage Co. is a waste disposal company that manages a fleet of drivers and garbage trucks that go to residential homes, collect garbage, and then dump the garbage in city landfills. They have an obligation to collect each home's garbage once a week. Recently, they have been failing to meet this requirement and are backed up with garbage disposal requests. What is causing this issue and what should they do to fix it?

Solution to #7: For cases involving processes and efficiencies, it can be helpful to look at the different components or steps in the process. We can think about the process as: drivers get in their trucks, take a designated route, collect garbage at each stop, and then dispose of the garbage in the landfill.

- Supply of drivers and garbage trucks
  - o Are there enough drivers to meet demand?
  - o Are there enough trucks to meet demand?

- Route efficiency
  - Are the garbage routes designed efficiently?
  - Are drivers driving too slowly or getting lost?

- Efficiency of collecting garbage
  - Does collecting garbage take too long?
  - Is there anything slowing workers down?

- Efficiency of disposing of garbage
  - Does disposing of the garbage take too long?
  - Is there anything slowing workers down?

Once you have systematically listed all of the steps in the overall garbage collection process, you can identify the pain point or bottleneck that is causing the issue.

Case framework problem #8: Hearts4Lives is a non-profit blood bank. They have volunteer nurses that go to schools and companies to collect blood from donors. They then sell this blood to hospitals, which use this blood for emergency situations when a blood transfusion is required. Currently, Hearts4Lives is not profitable because they are not able to collect enough blood to sell to their hospital partners. What can they do to fix this?

Solution to #8: This case involves many different stakeholders, such as the volunteer nurses, the blood donors, and the hospitals. For cases in which many different parties are involved, it may be useful to consider looking at each party and what each can do to help address the problem. One potential framework could look like the following:

- Increase nurse participation
  - Can we get more nurses to volunteer to collect blood?
  - Can we get nurses to work more hours to collect blood?

- Increase school and company participation
  - Can we get more schools to participate?
  - Can we get more companies to participate?

- Increase individual donor participation
  - Can we get each donor to donate a higher volume of blood?
  - Can we get donors to donate more frequently?

- Hospital partners
  - For existing hospital partners, can we sell the blood at a higher price?
  - Can we look for new hospital partners that would buy blood for a higher price?

Case problem #9: Pharma Co. is a pharmaceutical company that has just received Federal Drug Administration (FDA) approval for their new drug, Valos. This drug treats dry, cracking skin among patients that have eczema, a health condition that makes skin red and itchy. Pharma Co. has six months until the drug is expected to launch and wants to focus on efforts to increase drug adoption upon launch. How can Pharma Co. increase adoption of their new drug?

Solution framework to #9: The healthcare space is generally a complicated industry with many stakeholders. To increase adoption of Pharma Co.'s new drug, it may be helpful to consider all of the different stakeholders in the healthcare industry to see how each can be influenced.

The main stakeholders are patients, physicians, insurers, and Pharma Co. itself. There are many more stakeholders in healthcare, but these are the primary ones. A potential framework could look like the following:

- Increasing patient adoption
  - Increase patient awareness for Valos
  - Incentivize patients to ask their physicians for Valos

- Increasing physician adoption
  - Increase physician awareness for Valos
  - Incentivize physicians to recommend Valos to patients

- Increasing insurer adoption
  - Ensure insurers will reimburse or cover the drug
  - Incentivize insurers to promote the drug to hospitals

- Pharma Co. capabilities
  - Ensure that Pharma Co. can produce a sufficient quantity of the drug to meet demand
  - Ensure that Pharma Co. can deliver the drug on time to distributors

Case framework problem #10: HyperScale is a high-technology company that produces innovative and powerful smartphones in the market. They primarily sell their smartphones in the US. Historically, they release one new phone each year. They have just released this year's newest smartphone, the BoltX. Hyperscale is looking to grow at 30-40% per year over the next 10 years. How can they do this?

Solution to #10: This case is asking you to find aggressive strategies for growth. We can first think of growth as inorganic growth (growth through acquisition or partnership) and organic growth (growth by increasing output or sales internally). For organic growth, we can categorize growth as either growth through existing products or growth through new products.

Keeping this general structure in mind, one potential framework could look like the following.

- Growth through acquisition or partnership
  - Are there any attractive acquisition targets for HyperScale?
  - Are there any attractive partnerships that HyperScale could enter?

- Growth through increasing sales of existing products
  - Can Hyperscale sell their product to new customer segments?
  - Can Hyperscale sell their product through new distribution channels?
  - Can Hyperscale sell their product in other countries?

- Growth through sales of new products or services
    - o Are there other adjacent products that Hyperscale can produce and sell?
    - o Are there adjacent services that Hyperscale can provide to customers?

Case framework problem #11: Industrial Co. is a manufacturer of car parts for several automakers. They primarily make one car component called the car chassis, which is the main supporting frame for a vehicle. This car component is made of carbon steel. They purchase steel from a distributor and use machines and human labor to produce the chassis in their factories. They then ship the final product to automaker factories for automakers to use to fully assemble a car. Industrial Co. is looking to reduce costs by 25% over the next 5 years. How can they do this?

Solution to #11: This case is asking for strategies for cost reduction. Again, for cases that have complex processes, it may be helpful to break the process down into simpler components and consider each individually.

In this case, the major components are: sourcing steel from suppliers, using machines and human labor to produce the chassis, and shipping the chassis to automakers. Additionally, we can consider general overhead that is not related to the production process, such as corporate buildings. One potential framework could look like the following:

- Sourcing of raw materials
    - o Can a lower price be negotiated for steel?
    - o Can a cheaper alternative to steel be used?

- Production of chassis
    - o Can we pay workers a lower wage?
    - o Can the production process be more automated to reduce dependence on human labor?
    - o Is there cheaper or more efficient equipment that can be used?

- Delivery of chassis
  - Can shipping costs be reduced through an alternative and cheaper means of transportation?
  - Can we further optimize the delivery route and schedule to automakers?

- General overhead
  - Can the rent for Industrial Co.'s factories be negotiated down?
  - Can Industrial Co. decrease utilities costs?
  - Can other corporate overhead be reduced? (e.g., executive salaries, HR department)

Case framework problem #12: A wealthy CEO of a popular music label is considering starting an entertainment company that hosts massive, multi-day music festivals and concerts. These events would take place in isolated, but attractive locations, such as in a desert or on a private island.

Before deciding whether to consider this venture seriously, the CEO wants to learn more about the music festival space to be better informed. What are a few areas that the CEO should look into to assess and learn more about the music festival space?

Solution to #12: This case has quite a bit of overlap with your classic market entry case. Phrased another way, this case asks "what things would you need to know about the music festival space before deciding whether or not to enter?" Unlike the classic market entry case, we are more focused on understanding the market and competitors than we are in understanding the potential profitability of the venture. One potential framework could look like the following.

- Music festival market attractiveness
  - What is the market size?
  - What is the market growth rate?
  - What are average profit margins in this market?

- Music festival competitive landscape
  - How many major players are there?

- o How much market share does each player have?
- o What differentiation or competitive advantages do competitors have?

- Customer needs and preferences
  - o What are customers looking for in a music festival?
  - o What are customer purchasing behaviors?

- Risks
  - o What are the major risks involved in running a music festival?
  - o What is required to mitigate these risks?

Case framework problem #13: The city of Salt Lake City is considering hosting the next Winter Olympics. Should they do this?

Solution to #13: While brainstorming potential benefits and costs for hosting the Winter Olympics, it is important to consider both economic and non-economic benefits and costs. Beyond the profits that the city would get from hosting the Olympics, there are also benefits such as increased future tourism and an increase in morale for city residents. Beyond the explicit investment costs, there are also non-economic costs tied to things such as traffic or pollution.

One potential framework for this case could look like the following:

- Salt Lake City capabilities
  - o Does Salt Lake City have the infrastructure and capital to host the Winter Olympics?
  - o What investments or renovations does Salt Lake City need to make to accommodate hosting the Winter Olympics?

- Expected profitability
  - o What are the expected revenues?
  - o What are the expected costs?
  - o How long will it take to break even on upfront investment costs?

- Non-economic benefits
    - o Will hosting the Olympics boost future tourism?
    - o Will hosting the Olympics boost morale for residents?

- Non-economic costs
    - o How will the increased traffic in the city impact day-to-day living?
    - o Will there be an increase in pollution or crime?

Case framework problem #14: An amusement park is considering adding a new roller coaster attraction to increase park admissions. This new roller coaster would feature having three consecutive vertical loops. Should this new roller coaster be added?

Solution to #14: In this case, the new roller coaster can effectively be seen as a "new product." Therefore, you might want to look into areas such as customer, competition, profitability, and the amusement park's capabilities to build and manage this new attraction. One potential framework could look like the following:

- Customer needs and preferences
    - o Do new roller coasters typically incentivize current customers to visit amusement parks more often?
    - o Do new roller coasters incentivize new customers to go to amusement parks?
    - o What do customers think of this new roller coaster?

- Competitor offerings
    - o How does the amusement park's current roller coaster offerings compare to that of competitors?
    - o Do competitors have a similar type of roller coaster?

- Amusement park's capabilities
    - o Does the amusement park have the space and capital to build this roller coaster?
    - o Does the amusement park have the capabilities to operate and maintain this attraction safely?

- Expected profitability
  - How much will adding this new roller coaster cost?
  - What is the expected increase in revenues?

Case framework problem #15: The government of Krokville has historically given citizens in poverty food stamps so that they can purchase food and living supplies from a select list of grocery and supermarket stores. Recently, these citizens on welfare have complained about the difficulty in finding grocery and supermarket stores that accept these food stamps. They have made a request to receive their welfare in cash instead. How should you think about deciding whether or not the government should issue food stamps or cash?

Solution to #15: When deciding between two options or strategies, it is helpful to first list out the criteria that you would use to evaluate the different options. You can use this as the main structure for your framework. One potential framework could look like the following:

- Ease of use among citizens
  - Which option would be easier for citizens to pick up?
  - Which option would be easier for citizens to trade in for food or living supplies?

- Effectiveness in providing food and living supplies
  - Which option has the higher likelihood that citizens will pick up their handouts?
  - Which option has the higher likelihood that handouts will be spent on food or living supplies?

- Costs to implement
  - How much does the food stamp program currently cost to implement?
  - How much would it cost to switch to and maintain running a cash-based welfare program?

- Potential risks
  - What are the potential risks for giving citizens cash?
  - What are the potential risks for sticking with the food stamp option?

Case framework problem #16: BankCorp is a US financial institution that provides checking and savings accounts, investment accounts, and credit cards to both businesses and individuals. They are trying to increase revenues and want to enter the credit card market in a foreign country. How should they think about selecting which country to enter?

Solution to #16: This case is similar to the classic market entry case. The nuance here is that instead of deciding whether or not to enter a particular market, you are deciding which country to enter for a particular market. Therefore, when you have your list of criteria for what makes a country attractive, you need to compare that among all of the countries in consideration. One potential framework could look like the following:

- Attractiveness of each country
    - What is the credit card market size in each country?
    - What is the credit card market growth rate in each country?
    - What are average profit margins for credit cards in each country?

- Competitiveness in each country
    - How many credit card players are in each country?
    - How concentrated are credit card players in each country?
    - How high are barriers to entry in each country?

- BankCorp's ability to execute in each country
    - How strong are BankCorp's capabilities in each country?
    - Can BankCorp better leverage synergies in certain countries over others?

- Expected profitability in each country
    - What are the expected revenues in each country?
    - What are the expected costs in each country?
    - How long would it take for BankCorp to break even in each country?

Case framework problem #17: The average driver in London sits through over 200 hours of traffic each year. In order to reduce the amount of time drivers waste sitting in traffic, the city government is considering adding an additional highway lane to London's most congested highways. How should you think about considering whether or not this would be a good idea?

Solution to #17: There are multiple factors that need to be considered. The first is considering the impact that an additional highway lane would have on drivers. Another consideration is whether or not it is even feasible to add a highway lane. Finally, we need to consider whether adding an additional highway lane is the best way to reduce traffic. Are there other initiatives that could do an even better job of reducing traffic congestion?

These three considerations form the basis of a potential framework.

- Impact on drivers
  - How much would traffic be reduced if additional highway lanes are added?
  - Would adding additional lanes incentivize more drivers to drive, thereby increasing traffic?
  - How would adding additional lanes impact car accident rates?

- Feasibility of adding additional highway lanes
  - Does the city have sufficient funding to build these additional highway lanes?
  - Is there sufficient space to build these highway lanes?
  - Can the city afford to close parts of the highway in order to build these lanes?

- Alternative options
  - Is this initiative the best way to reduce traffic?
  - Are there other ways to better reduce traffic?

Market Sizing & Estimation Questions

The most famous consulting market sizing or estimation question is: how many golf balls fit in a standard airplane? Market sizing or estimation questions like this one may seem daunting, but can actually be quite simple with enough repetition and practice.

With market sizing or estimation questions, the interviewer is not looking for whether or not you have the correct answer or if your answer is even close. What they care about most is that you can structure a logical approach to the problem, execute on the math proficiently, and clearly communicate your thinking and the steps you took towards solving the problem.

Whenever you are given a market sizing or estimation problem, resist the temptation to jump right into doing calculations. Always take the time to structure your approach to the problem first. You can even ask the interviewer for a minute or two to collect your thoughts and structure an approach.

Once you have your approach, walk the interviewer through it to see if the interviewer agrees. If the interviewer does not agree with your approach, make adjustments to your approach based on the feedback the interviewer provided. If they do, simply follow your structure and begin doing the math and calculations.

At this point, the rest of the problem is simple arithmetic. You just need to make reasonable assumptions and perform the calculations correctly. Make sure to pay attention to missing zeroes or misplaced decimal places. These types of mistakes are the most common and will change your answer by an order of magnitude.

In the end, once you have your final answer, do a quick sense check to see if that number makes sense to you. Try to benchmark the number to a related statistic or figure that you know.

Market sizing problem #1: What is the market size of regular (disposable, non-electric) toothbrushes in the US?

Solution to #1: Remember, market size is defined as the total dollars of sales of a product or service in one year. However, sometimes the interviewer will ask for market size in terms of the number of units sold. Unless told otherwise, assume that market size is expressed in terms of dollars of annual sales.

Secondly, remember to structure an approach to solve this market sizing problem before you make up any numbers or do any math. One potential structure could look like the following:

- Start with the US population

- Estimate what percentage of the population brushes their teeth

- Estimate what percentage of the population uses regular toothbrushes instead of electric toothbrushes

- Estimate how many toothbrushes the average person goes through in a year

- Estimate the cost per toothbrush

- Multiply all of these figures to determine the market size of regular toothbrushes in the US

Executing on the math, we will assume that there are roughly 320M people in the US.

Assume about 90% of the population brushes their teeth. The remaining 10% that don't include babies that don't have teeth and people that do have teeth, but choose not to brush their teeth. This leaves us with 90% * 320M = 288M people.

Assume that perhaps 25% of people use electric toothbrushes, and so 75% use regular toothbrushes. That leaves us with 75% * 288M = 216M people.

Let's estimate that the average person goes through 10 toothbrushes each year, or that they change their toothbrush a little over once per month. This means that 10 * 216M = 2.16B toothbrushes are purchased each year.

Assume that a regular toothbrush costs about $2. Therefore, the market size of toothbrushes in the US is $2 * 2.16B toothbrushes = $4.32B.

Market sizing problem #2: What is the market size of soft drinks or soda in the US?

Solution to #2: For this problem, it will be helpful to segment the US population by age. In other words, instead of estimating what percentage of the entire US population drinks soda, you'll split the US population into age groups and develop estimates for what percentage of each age group consumes soda.

Segmenting by age is probably the most common segmentation done in market sizing problems. The reason for segmentation is that by considering each age group separately, you can develop more refined assumptions and estimates that ultimately should lead to a more accurate number.

The easiest way to segment the US population by age is to assume that the average human life expectancy is 80 years, with a uniform distribution of ages. You can break the population into four age groups, 0 to 20-year-olds, 21 to 40-year-olds, 41 to 60-year-olds, and 61 to 80-year-olds.

If you assume that the US population is 320M people, this means that there are 80M people in each age group (320M population / 4 age groups = 80M).

Given this suggestion, one potential structure could look like the following:

- Start with the US population

- Segment the US population by age group

- For each age group, estimate the percentage that drinks soda

- Sum these figures to calculate the number of people in the US that drink soda

- Segment soda drinkers into high-consumption and low-consumption soda drinkers

- Estimate the number of sodas consumed by high-consumption and low-consumption soda drinkers each year

- Sum these figures to calculate the number of sodas consumed in a year

- Estimate the average price per can of soda

- Multiply to determine the market size of soda in the US

Let's start with the US population of 320M. We'll segment the population into four age groups, 0 to 20-year-olds, 21 to 40-year-olds. 41 to 60-year-olds, and 61 to 80-year-olds. There are 320M / 4 = 80M people in each age group.

Soda consumption is typically highest among kids and typically declines as people age. Therefore, let's assume the following:

- 75% of 0 to 20-year-olds consume soda

- 50% of 21 to 40-year-olds consume soda

- 50% of 41 to 60-year-olds consume soda

- 25% of 61 to 80-year-olds consume soda

Since each age group has 80M people, this gives us the following:

- 75% * 80M = 60M soda drinkers in the first age group

- 50% * 80M = 40M soda drinkers in the second age group

- 50% * 80M = 40M soda drinkers in the third age group

- 25% * 80M = 20M soda drinkers in the fourth age group

Adding these together, we have 60M + 40M + 40M + 20M = 160M soda drinkers.

Among soda drinkers, let's estimate that 20% are high-consumption drinkers and 80% are low-consumption drinkers. This means that 160M * 20% = 32M are high-consumption drinkers and the remaining 128M are low-consumption drinkers.

Let's assume that high-consumption drinkers will drink two cans a day. Perhaps they will consume 700 cans of soda each year. That equates to 32M people * 700 cans = 22.4B cans of soda.

Let's assume low-consumption drinkers will drink almost one can a day. Perhaps they consume 300 cans of soda each year. That equates to 128M people * 300 cans = 38.4B cans of soda.

Summing the number of cans of soda consumed by high-consumption and low-consumption drinkers, we get 22.4B cans + 38.4B cans = 60.8B cans of soda.

The average price per can of soda is approximately $1 per can. Therefore, the market size for soda in the US is 60.8B cans * $1 per can = $60.8B.

Market sizing problem #3: How many TV ads are shown in the US each day?

Solution to #3: We'll first develop an approach to solve this problem. One potential structure could look like the following:

- Estimate the number of TV channels in the US

- Assume each channel is on-air for 24 hours each day

- Estimate the percentage of airtime that is given to ads

- Estimate the average duration of an ad

- Divide total ad airtime by ad duration to determine how many TV ads are shown in the US

Starting with the number of TV channels in the US, let's assume there are roughly 2,000 TV channels in the US.

Assuming each channel is on-air for 24 hours each day, that gives us 2,000 * 24 = 48,000 hours of airtime each day.

Based on personal experience, ads take up approximately 1/4 of total airtime. Therefore, ads run for 1/4 * 48,000 = 12,000 hours each day.

The average duration of an ad can be estimated to be approximately 30 seconds. Therefore, we need to divide 12,000 hours by 30 seconds to get the total number of ads run in a day.

12,000 hours is the equivalent of 60 * 12,000 = 720,000 minutes. 30 seconds is equivalent to 0.5 minutes.

So, 720,000 minutes divided by 0.5 minutes gives us <u>1.44M TV ads</u> that are shown in the US each day.

Market sizing problem #4: What is the volume of beer (in oz.) sold at an NBA basketball game?

Solution to #4: One approach we can use to structure this problem is the following:

- Estimate the average number of seats at an NBA basketball game

- Estimate the average percentage of seats that are filled

- Estimate the percentage of people that are legally allowed to drink beer

- Estimate the percentage of people that would buy beer at an NBA basketball game

- Estimate the average number of beers purchased per person

- Estimate the volume of one beer

- Multiply all of these figures to determine the volume of beer sold at an NBA basketball game

Let's estimate that the average NBA basketball arena has 20,000 seats. Assume that, on average, 70% of seats are filled. This means 70% * 20,000 = 14,000 people attend the average NBA basketball game.

Alcohol cannot be sold to people under the age of 21 in the US. If we assume that the average human life expectancy is 80 years and that there is a uniform distribution of ages, that means 20 / 80 = 25% of people cannot drink. Therefore, 75% of people can drink.

75% * 14,000 people = 10,500 people legally allowed to drink beer.

Let's estimate that perhaps 60% of these people would purchase a beer. That means 60% * 10,500 people = 6,300 people purchase beer.

If the average person purchases 1 beer, that means 6,300 beers are purchased.

One beer is approximately 12 oz. Therefore, 6,300 beers * 12 oz. = 75,600 oz. of beer is sold at an NBA basketball game.

Market sizing problem #5: How many iPhones does Apple sell in one day?

Solution to #5: For this problem, it is easier to start with the market size of cellphones in the US in terms of quantity of units and then estimate the percentage of market share that Apple has. From this, we can divide by 365 to get the number of iPhones sold in a day.

If you started with the number of Apple stores and then estimated how many iPhones each store sold, that structure also works. However, this method is more difficult because it is tough to estimate how many iPhones a store sells in one day.

Using the first approach, one potential structure to solve this problem could look like the following:

- Start with the US population

- Estimate the percentage of people that have cell phones

- Estimate the frequency in which people buy cell phones

- Calculate the number of cell phones purchased in the US each year

- Estimate the percentage of people that have iPhones instead of other cell phones

- Divide by 365 to get the number of iPhones Apple sells in one day

Let's assume that the US population is 320M people. Estimate that perhaps 75% of the population has cell phones. That means 75% * 320M = 240M people have cell phones.

Assume that people buy cell phones every 3 years. Therefore, 240M / 3 = 80M cell phones are purchased each year.

Estimate that Apple has about 20% market share in the cell phone market. That means, 20% * 80M cell phones = 16M iPhones are sold in the US each year.

Dividing by the number of days in a year, 16M iPhones / 365 = 43,835 iPhones sold each day. Let's round that figure to approximately 44,000 iPhones sold each day.

Market sizing problem #6: How many tires are sold in the US each year for personal vehicles?

Solution to #6: One potential structure for this problem could look like the following:

- Start with the US population

- Estimate the average number of people per household

- Estimate the percentage of households that own cars

- Of those households, estimate the average number of cars owned

- Multiply by four wheels

- Estimate the frequency in which wheels are replaced

- Multiply all of these figures to determine the number of tires sold in the US each year for personal vehicles

Let's start with a US population size of 320M. We can estimate that the average US household has 2.5 people. Therefore, there are 320M / 2.5 = 128M households in the US.

Estimate that about 75% of US households own a car. That gives us 75% * 128M households = 96M households.

Among households that own a car, the average number of cars owned is about 1.5 cars per household. Therefore, 1.5 cars * 96M households = 144M cars.

Each car has 4 tires, so there are 4 * 144M cars = 576M tires for personal vehicles in the US.

Tires are replaced approximately once every five years. Therefore, in a given year 576M tires / 5 = 115.2M tires are sold. We can round this to approximately <u>115M tires</u> sold in the US each year for personal vehicles.

Market sizing problem #7: How many airplanes take off from Los Angeles Airport (LAX) each day?

Solution to #7: One potential structure for this estimation problem could look like the following:

- Estimate the number of hours in a day when planes can take off from an airport

- Estimate what percentage of takeoff time is high-traffic takeoff vs. low-traffic takeoff

- Estimate the average time between takeoffs during the high-traffic takeoff period and low-traffic takeoff period

- Calculate the number of airplanes that take off from LAX each day

Let's assume that airplanes can take off from LAX between 6AM and the following 2AM. This gives us 20 hours of takeoff time.

A high volume of takeoffs occurs between 9AM and 5PM, which gives us 8 hours of high-traffic takeoff time. The remaining 12 hours can be considered low-traffic takeoff time.

During high-traffic takeoff time, let's assume 1 airplane takes off every minute. Therefore, 8 hours * 60 minutes * 1 takeoff per minute = 480 takeoffs.

During low-traffic takeoff time, let's assume 1 airplane takes off every 3 minutes. Therefore, 12 hours * 60 minutes * 1/3 takeoffs per minute = 240 take offs.

Adding these two figures together, 480 takeoffs + 240 takeoffs = <u>720 takeoffs</u> per day from Los Angeles Airport.

Market sizing problem #8: How much does a hair salon with five stylists make a week?

Solution to #8: One potential structure for this problem could look like the following.

- Start with five stylists

- Estimate the number of hours they work in a given day

- Estimate the number of days they work per week

- Estimate the percentage of time that they are busy cutting hair

- Estimate the average time it takes to cut someone's hair

- Divide to calculate the number of haircuts given

- Estimate the price per haircut

- Multiply to determine how much a hair salon with five stylists makes a week

Starting with 5 stylists, assume each stylist works 8 hours a day and 6 days a week. That gives us 5 stylists * 8 hours per day * 6 days = 240 hours worked a week.

Let's estimate that these stylists are kept busy about 75% of the time. During the rest of the 25% of the time, these stylists are not seeing customers and are waiting around. Therefore, this gives us 75% * 240 hours = 180 hours actively spent cutting hair.

The average haircut takes approximately 30 minutes to complete, or 0.5 hours. So, 180 hours / 0.5 hours per haircut = 360 haircuts given per week.

The average haircut can be estimated to be about $25. Therefore, the hair salon makes 360 haircuts * $25 per haircut = $9,000 per week.

Market sizing problem #9: How many golf balls fit in a standard airplane?

Solution to #9: While this may sound like a daunting problem, the structure for this problem is actually quite simple. At its core, we need to find the volume of an airplane and divide that by the volume of a golf ball. We can use basic geometry to make these calculations. One simple structure could be the following:

- Estimate the volume of an airplane
  - Model an airplane as a rectangular prism, with volume = length * width * height
  - Estimate an airplane's length, height, and width
  - Estimate what percentage of an airplane is empty space vs. space that is occupied by seats
  - Multiply these figures to determine the volume of an airplane that can fit golf balls

- Estimate the volume of a golf ball
  - Model a golf ball as a sphere, with volume = $(4/3) * \pi * (radius)^3$
  - Estimate the diameter of a golf ball
  - Convert the diameter to a radius
  - Calculate the volume of a golf ball

- Divide the volume of an airplane by the volume of a golf ball to determine the number of golf balls that will fit

Let's start by calculating the volume of an airplane. We can estimate that its length is 100 ft, width is 10 ft, and height is 10 ft. That makes the volume 100 ft * 10 ft * 10 ft = 10,000 cubic feet.

Let's assume that 80% of the volume of an airplane is empty space and the remaining 20% is occupied by solid things, such as seats. Therefore, the empty space in an airplane is 80% * 10,000 cubic feet = 8,000 cubic feet.

Moving onto calculating the volume of a golf ball, we can estimate that the diameter of a golf ball to be about 1.5 inches in diameter. Therefore, the radius is 0.75 inches, half of the diameter.

The volume of a sphere = $(4/3) * \pi * (radius)^3$. So, $(4/3) * (3.14) * (0.75)^3 = 1.77$ cubic inches.

Next, we'll need to convert from cubic inches to cubic feet. Because there are 12 inches in a foot, that means there are 12 * 12 * 12 cubic inches in a cubic foot. So, 1.77 cubic inches / (12 * 12 * 12) = 0.001 cubic feet. This is the volume of a golf ball in units of cubic feet.

Finally, we'll divide the volume of an airplane by the volume of a golf ball to get our answer. 8,000 cubic feet / 0.001 cubic feet = <u>8M golf balls</u> that can fit in a standard airplane.

The answer that you calculated will likely be very different, depending on the assumptions that you make. However, remember that the most important part of these market sizing or estimation questions is that you develop a logical, structured approach and that you execute on the math proficiently.

Market sizing problem #10: What is the length of spaghetti consumed in the US each year? Use inches for your units.

Solution to #10: Again, this problem may seem difficult and tedious, but once you break down the problem into smaller, simpler steps, the problem becomes much easier. Here is one structured approach you could use:

- Start with the US population

- Estimate the percentage of people that eat spaghetti

- Segment these people into high-frequency and low-frequency spaghetti consumers

- Estimate the frequency in which high-frequency and low-frequency consumers eat spaghetti each year

- Calculate the number of spaghetti meals in the US each year

- For the average meal, estimate how many bites are taken

- For the average bite, estimate how many strands of spaghetti are consumed

- Estimate the length of an average strand of spaghetti

- Multiply these figures to determine the length of spaghetti consumed in the US each year

Starting with a US population size of 320M, let's estimate that 75% of people eat spaghetti. That gives us 75% * 320M = 240M people.

Among these 240M people, let's estimate that 25% eat spaghetti with high-frequency and 75% eat spaghetti with low-frequency. Therefore, there are 60M high-frequency consumers and 180M low-frequency consumers.

Let's estimate that high-frequency consumers eat spaghetti three times a week, or about 150 times a year. Therefore, high-frequency consumers account for 60M * 150 = 9B spaghetti meals.

Let's estimate that low-frequency consumers eat spaghetti a little less than once a month, or roughly 10 times a year. Therefore, low-frequency consumers account for 180M * 10 = 1.8B spaghetti meals.

The total number of spaghetti meals is 9B + 1.8B = 10.8B.

For the average meal, let's assume that 10 bites are needed to finish the meal. In each bite, we'll assume there are 5 spaghetti strands. Therefore, the average meal contains 10 bites * 5 strands per bite = 50 strands of spaghetti.

10.8B spaghetti meals * 50 strands of spaghetti per meal = 540B strands of spaghetti.

The average spaghetti strand length is 10 inches. Therefore, the length of spaghetti consumed in the US each year is 540B strands of spaghetti * 10 inches length per strand = <u>5.4T inches</u>.

Profitability Questions

Profitability questions are quantitative problems that test your understanding of two basic concepts, profit and profitability. If you know and practice using equations related to these concepts, these problems should be simple.

The first concept you need to know is profit. There are a set of basic profit-related equations you should fully know and understand:

- Profit = Revenue – Costs

- Revenue = Quantity * Price

- Costs = Variable Costs + Fixed Costs

- Variable Costs = Quantity * Variable Cost

- Profit = [(Price – Variable Cost) * Quantity] – Fixed Costs

The next concept you need to know is profitability or profit margin. Profitability and profit margin are often used synonymously. The main profitability or profit margin equation is:

- Profitability or Profit Margin = (Revenue – Costs) / Revenue

There are two types of profit margins, gross profit margin and operating profit margin. Gross profit margin calculates the profitability that only takes into account the cost of goods sold (variable costs). Operating profit margin calculates the profitability taking into account both cost of goods sold and overhead or other operating costs (fixed costs).

Profitability problem #1: Cereal Co. produces three varieties of cereals. Their first cereal, Frosted Crisps, sells for $4.50 per box. Their second cereal, Choco Puffs, sells for $3.50 per box. Their third cereal, Lucky Flakes, sells for $2.50 per box. All of these cereals cost $0.50 per box to produce.

Cereal Co. sells their cereals throughout 1,000 different supermarkets and convenience stores in the US. On average, in each store, they sell 20 boxes of Frosted Crisps per week, 20 boxes of Choco Puffs per week, and 40 boxes of Lucky Flakes per week. Assume that these stores operate 50 weeks each year.

To produce cereal, Cereal Co. owns a factory that costs $30M to own, manage, and operate. Assume that Cereal Co. can spread this cost evenly over 10 years. Additionally, Cereal Co. has 100 employees, who on average, are paid $50K in wages per year.

How much profit does Cereal Co. generate each year?

Solution to #1: We'll start by calculating the profit generated by each cereal variety. Then, we'll subtract the remaining costs from the aggregated profit to determine the overall profits for the company.

In order to calculate the profit generated by each cereal variety, we first need to calculate the quantity sold per year.

- Frosted Crisps quantity sold = 1,000 stores * 50 weeks * 20 boxes sold per week = 1M boxes sold

- Choco Puffs quantity sold = 1,000 stores * 50 weeks * 20 boxes sold per week = 1M boxes sold

- Lucky Flakes quantity sold = 1,000 stores * 50 weeks * 40 boxes sold per week = 2M boxes sold

Since we know the price that each cereal is sold for and how much each cereal box costs to produce, we can calculate profit for each cereal.

- Frosted Crisps profit = 1M * ($4.50 - $0.50) = $4M

- Choco Puffs profit = 1M * ($3.50 - $0.50) = $3M

- Lucky Flakes profit = 2M * ($2.50 - $0.50) = $4M

- Total profit from all cereals = $4M + $3M + $4M = $11M

Next, we'll sum up the remaining costs. Remember that the $30M cost for the factory can be spread out evenly over 10 years.

- Factory fixed costs = $30M / 10 = $3M per year

- Employee costs = 100 * $50K = $5M per year

- Total costs = $8M

Taking the profits from cereals, $11M, and subtracting the remaining costs, $8M, we get that Cereal Co.'s annual profits are $3M.

Profitability problem #2: Continuing on from the example in the previous problem, assume that Cereal Co. sells 1M boxes of Frosted Crips and 1M boxes of Choco Puffs in a given year. How many boxes of Lucky Flakes would Cereal Co. need to sell in order to break even?

Solution to #2: For breakeven problems, we set overall profits equal to zero and solve for the unknown variable. In this problem, the unknown variable is the quantity of Lucky Flakes boxes sold. We know the following already:

- Profit from cereals
  - Frosted Crisps profit = 1M * ($4.50 - $0.50) = $4M
  - Choco Puffs profit = 1M * ($3.50 - $0.50) = $3M
  - Lucky Flakes profit = Q * ($2.50 - $0.50) = $2Q

- Fixed Costs
    - Factory fixed costs = $30M / 10 = $3M per year
    - Employee costs = 100 * $50K = $5M per year

Note that for Lucky Flakes, we left the number of boxes sold as an unknown variable, designated by the variable "Q." We can now set up an equation for Cereal Co.'s profit and set profit equal to zero in order to solve for this unknown variable.

Profit = $4M + $3M + $2Q - $3M - $5M
0 = $4M + $3M + $2Q - $3M - $5M
0 = -$1M + $2Q
$2Q = $1M
Q = 500K

Therefore, Cereal Co. needs to sell 500K boxes of Lucky Flakes in order to break even.

Profitability problem #3: Continuing on with this example for Cereal Co., assume the following information:

- Frosted Crisps
    - Price = $4.50
    - Cost of goods sold = $0.50
    - Quantity sold = 1M

- Choco Puffs
    - Price = $3.50
    - Cost of goods sold = $0.50
    - Quantity sold = 1M

- Lucky Flakes
    - Price = $2.50
    - Cost of goods sold= $0.50
    - Quantity sold = 2M

- Fixed Costs
    - Factory = $3M
    - Employee = $5M

What is the gross profit margin and operating profit margin for Cereal Co.?

Solution to #3: Let's calculate the gross profit margin first. Remember that the gross profit margin calculates profitability by only taking into account the cost of goods sold. To calculate the profit margin, we need to calculate total revenues and total cost of goods sold.

Total revenues can be calculated by multiplying the price of each cereal with the quantity sold.

Revenue = ($4.50 * 1M) + ($3.50 * 1M) + ($2.50 * 2M)
Revenue = $4.5M + $3.5M + $5M
Revenue = $13M

The total cost of goods sold can be calculated by multiplying the cost of goods sold for each cereal by the quantity sold.

Cost of goods sold = ($0.50 * 1M) + ($0.50 * 1M) + ($0.50 * 2M)
Cost of goods sold = $0.5M + $0.5M + $1M
Cost of goods sold = $2M

Finally, we can calculate the gross profit margin.

Gross profit margin = (Revenue – Cost of Goods Sold) / Revenue
Gross profit margin = ($13M - $2M) / $13M
Gross profit margin = $11M / $13M
Gross profit margin = 85% (rounded)

Moving onto calculating the operating profit margin, the only adjustment we need to make is to add fixed and operating costs into our calculations. The cost of goods sold was previously calculated to be $2M, so we will add $3M for factory costs and $5M for employee costs.

Total Costs = Cost of goods sold + Factory costs + Employee costs
Total Costs = $2M + $3M + $5M
Total Costs = $10M

Operating profit margin = (Revenue – Costs) / Revenue
Operating profit margin = ($13M –$10M) / $13M
<u>Operating profit margin = 23% (rounded)</u>

Note that the operating profit margin is much lower than the gross profit margin. This is because there are substantial fixed and operating costs for this business.

Profitability problem #4: Continuing on with this example for Cereal Co., assume the following information:

- Frosted Crisps
    - Price = $4.50
    - Cost of goods sold = $0.50
    - Quantity sold = 1M

- Choco Puffs
    - Price = $3.50
    - Cost of goods sold = $0.50
    - Quantity sold = 1M

- Lucky Flakes
    - Price = ???
    - Cost of goods sold= $0.50
    - Quantity sold = 2M

What must the price of Lucky Flakes be in order for Cereal Co. to generate an overall gross profit margin of 90%?

Solution to #4: For this problem, we will take the formula for gross profit margin and set it equal to 90%. We can then solve for the one unknown, the price of Lucky Flakes. We'll indicate this unknown variable as "P."

Since we are dealing with the gross profit margin, we'll need to calculate the total revenue and cost of goods sold.

Revenue = ($4.50 * 1M) + ($3.50 * 1M) + ($P * 2M)
Revenue = $4.5M + $3.5M + (2M * $P)
Revenue = $8M + (2M * $P)

52

Cost of goods sold = ($0.50 * 1M) + ($0.50 * 1M) + ($0.50 * 2M)
Cost of goods sold = $0.5M + $0.5M + $1M
Cost of goods sold = $2M

Let's plug revenue and cost of goods sold into our gross profit margin formula.

Gross profit margin = (Revenue – Cost of Goods Sold) / Revenue
Gross profit margin = [$8M + (2M * $P) - $2M] / [$8M + (2M * $P)]
0.9 = [$6M + (2M * $P)] / [$8M + (2M * $P)]
0.9 * [$8M + (2M * $P)] = [$6M + (2M * $P)]
$7.2M + (1.8M * $P) = $6M + (2M * $P)
$1.2M = (0.2M * $P)
P = $6

Lucky Flakes needs to be priced at <u>$6 per box</u> in order for Cereal Co. to have a gross profit margin of 90%.

Profitability problem #5: General Wheat is also a cereal producer with three different cereal products. Last year, they had the following performance:

- Cookie Flakes
  - o 25% of revenues
  - o Price = $3
  - o Cost of goods sold= $0.90

- Honey Oats
  - o 25% of revenues
  - o Price = $4
  - o Cost of goods sold= $2

- Almond Clusters
  - o 50% of revenues
  - o Price = $5
  - o Cost of goods sold= $1

This year, they had the following performance:

- Cookie Flakes
    - 25% of revenues
    - Price = $3
    - Cost of goods sold= $1.20

- Honey Oats
    - 35% of revenues
    - Price = $4
    - Cost of goods sold= $2

- Almond Clusters
    - 40% of revenues
    - Price = $5
    - Cost of goods sold= $2

How much did gross profit margins change by from last year to this year?

Solution to #5: To find the change in profit margins, we'll first calculate profit margins last year and compare that to profit margins this year.

To calculate the company's overall profit margin last year, we'll first find the profit margins of each product.

Last year:

- Cookie Flakes profit margin = ($3 - $0.90) / $3 = 70%

- Honey Oats profit margin = ($4 - $2) / $4 = 50%

- Almond Clusters profit margin = ($5 - $1) / $5 = 80%

The overall profit margin for the company is simply a weighted average of the profit margins of each cereal. The weight of each product's profit margin is determined by the percentage of revenue.

Last year's profit = (25% * 70%) + (25% * 50%) + (50% * 80%)
Last year's profit = 70%

We can repeat this for this year's profit.

This year:

- Cookie Flakes profit margin = ($3 - $1.20) / $3 = 60%

- Honey Oats profit margin = ($4 - $2) / $4 = 50%

- Almond Clusters profit margin = ($5 - $2) / $5 = 60%

This year's profit = (25% * 60%) + (35% * 50%) + (40% * 60%)
This year's profit = 56.5%

Therefore, profits have declined from 70% to 56.5%, a <u>decrease of 13.5%</u>.

Profitability problem #6: Continuing on from the previous problem, what are the drivers that caused profitability to change?

Solution to #6: To solve this problem, we need to compare last year's performance with this year's performance and see what has changed.

From the information provided, we see three drivers or changes that caused a change in profit:

1. Cookie Flakes' cost of goods sold increased from $0.90 to $1.20 per box

2. Almond Clusters' cost of goods sold increased from $1 to $2 per box

3. A shift in the proportion of sales away from Almond Clusters, which decreased from 50% to 40% of revenues, and towards Honey Oats, which increased from 25% of revenues to 35% of revenues. Almond Clusters has a higher profit margin than Honey Oats.

Profitability problem #7: Based on the three drivers identified in the previous problem, which driver contributed the most to the decline in overall profits?

Solution to #7: To solve this problem, we need to isolate each of the three changes that occurred from last year to this year and see how much each individually contribute to the overall decline in profits.

Driver 1: Cookie Flakes' cost of goods sold increased from $0.90 to $1.20 per box

If we assume that this is the only change that occurred from last year to this year, we calculate the following. I've indicated the change in **bold**.

Last year's profit = (25% * 70%) + (25% * 50%) + (50% * 80%) = 70%
This year's profit = (25% * **60%**) + (25% * 50%) + (50% * 80%) = 67.5%

Therefore, the increase in the cost of goods sold of Cookie Flakes decreased profitability by 2.5%.

Driver 2: Almond Clusters' cost of goods sold increased from $1 to $2 per box

If we assume that this is the only change that occurred from last year to this year, we calculate the following. I've indicated the change in **bold**.

Last year's profit = (25% * 70%) + (25% * 50%) + (50% * 80%) = 70%
This year's profit = (25% * 70%) + (25% * 50%) + (50% * **60%**) = 60%

Therefore, the increase in the cost of goods sold of Almond Clusters decreased profitability by 10%.

Driver 3: A shift in the proportion of sales away from Almond Clusters, which decreased from 50% to 40% of revenues, and towards Honey Oats, which increased from 25% of revenues to 35% of revenues

The calculation for this driver is slightly different from the prior two. The reason for this is that the shift in the proportion of sales away from Almond Clusters and towards Honey Oats coincides or overlaps with the increase in the cost of goods sold of Almond Clusters. Therefore, if we individually calculate the change in profitability for this driver individually, we double count the decline in profitability.

To avoid double counting the decline in profitability, we need to set Almost Clusters' profit margin to be 60%, which is the new profit margin after the increase in the cost of goods sold.

Profit before sales mix change = (25% * 70%) + (25% * 50%) + (50% * **60%**) = 60%

Profit after sales mix change = (25% * 70%) + (**35%** * 50%) + (**40%** * **60%**) = 59%

Therefore, the shift in the proportion of sales away from Almond Clusters and towards Honey Oats decreased profitability by 1%.

To recap, each of the drivers individually causes the following decline in profitability:

- Increase in cost of goods sold of Cookie Flakes: 2.5% decline

- Increase in cost of goods sold of Almond Clusters: 10% decline

- A shift in the proportion of sales away from Almond Clusters and towards Honey Oats: 1% decline

Therefore, <u>the increase in the cost of goods sold of Almond Clusters</u> contributed the most to the overall decline in profitability.

Note that the sum of the three individual driver declines in profitability is 2.5% + 10% + 1% = 13.5%. This is exactly the overall profitability decline from last year to this year. Recall from the previous problem that overall profitability for General Wheat declined from 70% to 56.5%, or by 13.5%. This is a good check to do to ensure that you have performed the calculations correctly.

Profitability problem #8: General Wheat is currently only selling cereal in the US, but is considering entering Canada. They estimate that there is an 80% chance that the Canada market will be in a growth phase and a 20% chance that the Canada market will be in a decline phase.

If Canada is in a growth phase, General Wheat estimates that there is a 70% chance they will succeed and earn $10M in profits. They estimate that there is a 30% chance they will fail and will just barely break even on their costs.

If Canada is in a decline phase, General Wheat estimates that there is a 20% chance they will succeed and earn $5M in profits. They estimate that there is an 80% chance they will fail and lose $40M.

Should General Wheat enter the Canada market?

Solution to #8: This is an expected value problem. It can be solved by taking the probability that each event will happen and multiplying each by the expected profitability or loss in that event. Summing all of these products together will give you the expected value, or the average value you would expect.

Assuming that the Canada market will be in a growth phase, the expected value (EV) is calculated as:

EV if growth phase = (70% * $10M) + (30% * $0) = $7M

Assuming that the Canada market will be in a decline phase, the expected value (EV) is calculated as:

EV if decline phase = (20% * $5M) + (80% * -$40M) = -$31M

We can now take these expected values and compute an overall expected value, taking into account the fact that there is an 80% chance that Canada will be in a growth phase and a 20% chance that Canada will be in a decline phase.

Overall EV = (80% * $7M) + (20% * -$31M) = -$600K

Since the overall expected value is -$600K, <u>General Wheat should not enter the Canada market</u>.

Profitability problem #9: General Wheat is also considering adding a new cereal product, Maple Loops, to their product line. Maple Loops will be sold at $4 per box and has a cost of goods sold of $3 per box. They expect to sell 1M boxes of Maple Loops.

However, by introducing this new product, General Wheat expects to lose some sales of Cookie Flakes, Honey Oats, and Almond Clusters since some customers may switch over from purchasing these cereals to purchasing Maple Loops instead. They expect to lose sales on 100K boxes of Cookie Flakes, 200K boxes of Honey Oats, and 200K boxes of Almond Clusters.

Should General Wheat launch their new cereal, Maple Loops? Information on the price and cost of each cereal is given below.

- Cookie Flakes
    - Price = $3
    - Cost of goods sold= $1.20

- Honey Oats
    - Price = $4
    - Cost of goods sold= $2

- Almond Clusters
    - Price = $5
    - Cost of goods sold= $2

Solution to #9: This problem is a sales cannibalization problem. By adding a new product that has a low profit margin, we are increasing revenues through sales of this new cereal, but also taking away sales from the other cereals. The key question is whether the increase in sales from launching this new cereal is greater than the loss in sales caused by this cannibalization.

First, we will calculate the increase in profit from selling this new cereal.

Profit from new cereal = 1M * ($4 - $3) = $1M

Next, we will calculate the decrease in profit from losing sales in the other cereal brands.

Loss of profit from Cookie Flakes = 100K * ($3 - $1.20) = $180K
Loss of profit from Honey Oats = 200K * ($4 - $2) = $400K
Loss of profit from Almond Clusters = 200K * ($5 - $2) = $600K

Finally, we will calculate the net change in profit from launching this new cereal.

Net change in profit = $1M - $180K - $400K - $600K = -$180K

Since the net change in profit is negative, <u>General Wheat should not launch their new cereal</u>. The profit from sales of this new cereal is outweighed by sales cannibalization of existing higher margin cereals.

Interpreting Charts & Graphs

You should expect to see charts and graphs at some point during your case interview. Interviewers want to see that you are comfortable interpreting data and drawing meaningful insights.

Whenever you see a complicated or confusing chart, it is helpful to look at the axes first. What does each of the axes measure? Once you understand the axes, you can start understanding what the chart or graph is trying to show.

It is also helpful to talk through your thinking out loud. This can help the interviewer understand what you are thinking about and provides opportunities for the interviewer to correct you or provide hints if you are misinterpreting something. Try to avoid having too much silence during the case interview when you are looking at and analyzing charts and graphs.

Additionally, make sure you connect the data in the charts and graphs to the ultimate objective of the case. Don't just simply state which bar is the tallest or which segment is the largest. Instead, based on the data in front of you, how does this impact the recommendation or answer to the case? What differentiates great case interview candidates from average case interview candidates is going beyond the facts to form opinions and recommendations.

Finally, do not be surprised when you are handed several pages of handouts that contain different charts and graphs. Do not feel overwhelmed by this. Take your time talking through and analyzing each of the charts and graphs one at a time. Then, look at possible insights you can draw by connecting data from one chart or graph to another chart or graph. For cases in which you are given multiple charts and graphs, the key insight typically requires synthesizing data across multiple exhibits.

Charts & graphs problem #1: StayCay is a hotel booking website that allows customers to book hotels for either business travel or personal vacation. They have collected data on the number of rooms booked through their website and competitors' websites last week. What can you conclude about the competitive positioning of StayCay?

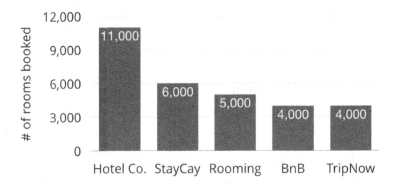

Solution to #1: This is a simple bar chart showing the number of rooms booked by each website last week.

Surface-level insights:

- Hotel Co. had the greatest number of rooms booked last week at 11,000 rooms

- StayCay had the second greatest number of rooms booked last week at 6,000 rooms

Deeper insights:

- The average number of rooms booked by each website is 6,000 (30,000 rooms / 5 players), which makes StayCay exactly average

- Hotel Co. has a significant scale advantage over other players. Even if StayCay acquired another player, they would be tied or still behind Hotel Co. in terms of number of rooms booked

- StayCay's closest competitors are likely Rooming, BnB, and TripNow since they are of similar size

Charts & graphs problem #2: Gracy's is a clothing retailer that has nearly 1,000 stores across the US. They have collected sales data from their own company and two rival companies. The sales data shows sales by each clothing segment (female, male, kids, and babies clothing). Based on the chart below, what can you conclude about the competitive positioning of Gracy's and their competitors?

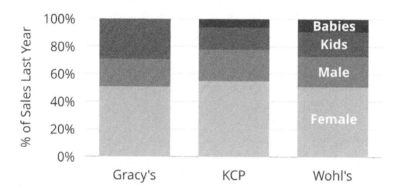

Solution to #2: This is a 100% stacked bar chart in which all of the segments within a bar add up to 100% of a company's sales last year. Rather than showing absolute size like a bar chart does, a 100% stacked bar chart shows relative proportions across bars.

In this chart, we see the relative proportion of sales that female, male, kids, and babies clothing make up as a percentage of total sales for three different clothing retailers.

Surface-level insights:

- Gracy's does not have a presence in the babies segment

- Gracy's has a higher proportion of sales coming from kids relative to competitors

- All players have a similar proportion of sales coming from female and male segments

Deeper insights:

- Gracy's could consider entering the babies segment as they already have a relatively high proportion of sales coming from the kids segment

Charts & graphs problem #3: CarZone performs car repair services for customers. They service a wide variety of car damages, ranging from lightly damaged vehicles to heavily damaged vehicles. The market for car repair services in the Philadelphia region is shown below. What insights can you draw?

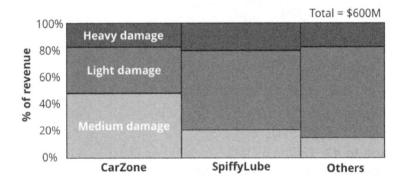

Solution to #3: This type of chart is known as a Marimekko or Mekko chart. The vertical segments or bars are identical to a 100% stacked bar chart. In this chart, the vertical segments show medium damage, light damage, and heavy damage repairs as a percentage of total revenue for a given company.

The additional information that a Mekko chart provides lies in the widths of the bars, which adds another dimension of information. In this chart, the widths show the proportion of the car repair services market that CarZone, SpiffyLube, and others make up.

Another way to think about this chart is that the entire chart is one large pie chart, in which the total size is $600M. Each segment represents a piece of the total pie. Segments with a larger area imply a higher share of the total market.

Surface-level insights:

- CarZone and SpiffyLube each have revenues of about $200M

- CarZone has the largest proportion of their revenues coming from medium damage repairs

- SpiffyLube and others have the largest proportion of their revenues coming from light damage repairs

- CarZone, SpiffyLube, and others have a similar proportion of sales coming from heavy damage repairs

Deeper insights:

- The car repair services market is highly concentrated, with the top two players having over two-thirds of the total market share

- CarZone is the clear market leader in medium damage repairs while SpiffyLube is the clear market leader in light damage repairs

- CarZone should determine why it is capturing a lower than expected share of the light damage repair market

Charts & graphs problem #4: Your client sells enterprise software to businesses that helps them manage their inventory. They have been tracking drivers that have impacted the number of customers they have had in the most recent fiscal year. Based on the chart below, what insights can you draw?

Solution to #4: This is a waterfall chart, which is a chart typically used to bridge two different numbers over a time period. The y-axis shows the number of customers. The x-axis shows different drivers that impact the number of customers. This waterfall chart bridges the number of customers in year one to the number of customers in year two. In other words, it shows what changes happened between year one and year two.

Surface-level insights:

- The total number of customers has decreased from 2,000 in year one to 1,700 in year two

- Mass marketing, targeted marketing, and referrals all contributed to an increase in the number of customers, with targeted marketing contributing the most

- Price increase and natural attrition contributed to a decrease in the number of customers, with price increase contributing the most

Deeper insights:

- Since targeted marketing contributes the most to the increase in customers, the company should consider prioritizing or investing more in this strategy

- If prices were not increased, the number of customers would have increased from 2,000 in year one to 2,900 in year two;

therefore, the company should investigate whether the increased revenue from increasing prices justifies the decrease in the number of customers

Charts & graphs problem #5: MoonTrust is a bank that provides diversified financial services to customers. One of the key drivers for their growth is the growth of their salesforce. MoonTrust's salesforce handles prospective new customers and tries to get them to sign up for one or more financial services. MoonTrust has collected the past thirteen years of annual revenue growth data below. Based on this graph, what insights can you draw?

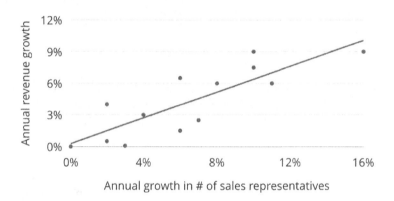

Annual growth in # of sales representatives

Solution to #5: This is a simple scatterplot with a trendline added. The trendline shows the relationship between the x-axis, which is the annual growth in the number of sales representatives, and the y-axis, which shows annual revenue growth.

Surface-level insights:

- There is a positive correlation between annual growth in the number of sales representatives and annual revenue growth

- For every 1% growth in the number of sales representatives, we should expect roughly 0.75% growth in annual revenue

Deeper insights:

- The positive correlation may only hold between the 0-12% range of annual growth in the number of sales representatives

- Beyond 12% annual growth in the number of sales representatives, we should be careful when predicting annual revenue growth since there are few data points

- This chart does not necessarily confirm that the growth in the number of sales representatives is what drives revenue growth. There could be another confounding factor

Charts & graphs problem #6: Your client, Unico, is a diversified consumer packaged goods company that sells a variety of home products to consumers. Their largest competitor is Testle, which sells similar home products to consumers. Based on the chart below, what insights can you draw on Unico's competitive positioning?

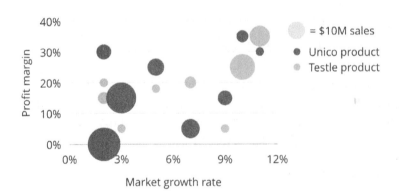

Solution to #6: This bubble chart shows four dimensions of information through the x-axis, y-axis, bubble size, and bubble color. The x-axis shows the market growth rate for each product while the y-axis shows the profit margin for each product. The size of the bubble shows the level of sales for each product. Finally, the color of the bubble shows whether the product is a Unico product or a Testle product.

When looking at bubble charts, it is helpful to identify which quadrant is most attractive or desirable. In this problem, we want to be selling products that have both a high profit margin and a high market growth rate. Therefore, the most attractive quadrant is the top right quadrant. Once we know this, we can start focusing on the other dimensions of information, such as bubble size and bubble color.

Surface-level insights:

- Unico is a larger player than Testle

- Both Unico and Testle have a wide range of products that have different product market growth rates and profit margins

- Testle has higher sales in products that have a high market growth rate and high profit margin

- Unico has higher sales in products that have low market growth rate and low profit margin

Deeper insights:

- Overall, Testle likely has a higher profit margin than Unico

- Unico should focus on selling more products that have high profit margins and high market growth rates

- Unico has one product that has a zero percent profit margin; they should investigate whether selling that product still makes sense given that the product is very close to being unprofitable

Charts & graphs problem #7: P&P, Fitzer, and Zerk are three pharmaceutical companies that were founded in the same year. Based on the following graph, what insights can you draw on each of their growth performances?

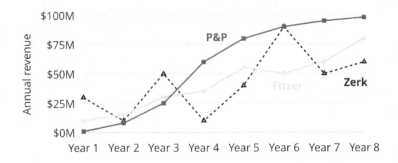

Solution to #7: This line graph shows how annual revenues have grown over eight years for three different pharmaceutical companies.

Surface-level insights:

- P&P has the highest annual revenue in year 8 despite starting with the lowest annual revenue in year 1

- Fitzer has the second highest annual revenue in year 8

- Zerk has the lowest annual revenue in year 8 despite starting with the highest annual revenue in year 1

Deeper insights:

- Fitzer's revenue has grown steadily over the past eight years, increasing by about $10M per year. Their trajectory suggests that this growth is expected to continue

- P&P's revenue growth follows a typical S-curve: revenues grew slowly in the earlier years, then grew rapidly in the middle years, and then finally slowed down in later years. Their trajectory suggests that their growth has plateaued

- Zerk has had the most volatile growth, with large jumps or drops in revenue year over year. This could be caused by selling products that have volatile pricing or by developing drugs that either boom or bust

Charts & graphs problem #8: Pillar manufacturers and sells lawn mowers to residential consumers. They recently conducted a consumer survey asking customers what attributes they value the most when selecting a lawn mower to purchase. They also asked customers to rate how Pillar and Steere, Pillar's primary competitor, perform on these attributes. Based on the chart below, what insights can you draw? The bars in the chart represent the level of importance that customers value each attribute while the lines represent the performance of Steere and Pillar on these attributes.

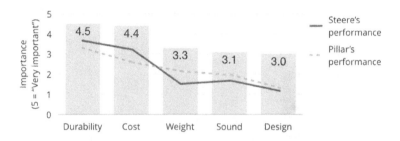

Solution to #8: This chart combines a bar chart and a line graph. First, we can look at each individually. Then, we can look at them collectively in order to draw appropriate insights.

Surface-level insights:

- Durability and cost are the attributes that customers value the most, substantially higher than the other attributes

- Steere performs better than Pillar on durability and cost, but Pillar performs better than Steere on weight, sound, and design

Deeper insights:

- Steere performs strongly on attributes that customers care most about, which are durability and cost

- Pillar should prioritize and invest in improving performance on the durability and cost attributes since customers don't value weight, sound, and design as highly

Charts & graphs problem #9: Allhands, is an insurance company that provides home, life, and car insurance to households in the US. They've pulled together some data on the number of insurance claims each household files per year. The average insurance claim costs Allhands $250. Based on the chart below, answer the following two questions:

- What percentage of households costs Allhands $750 or more per year?

- What is the expected number of claims filed per household?

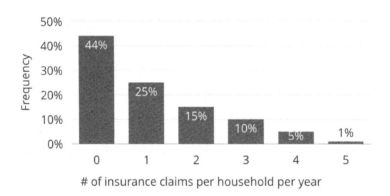

# of insurance claims per household per year

Solution to #9: This is a histogram, which shows the distribution of a variable. In this problem, that variable is the number of insurance claims filed per household per year. In a histogram, all of the bars will add up to 100%.

Looking at the first question, we are given that the average claim costs Allhands $250. If three claims are filed, then that gives us an average cost of $750. Therefore, we can reframe the question as asking what percentage of households file three or more claims per year. Adding the frequencies that three, four, and five claims are filed per household per year, we get 10% + 5% + 1% = 16%.

We expect <u>16%</u> of households to cost Allhands $750 or more.

Looking at the second question, we are asked to calculate the expected value (EV) based on the histogram. This can be done by taking the product of frequency and the number of insurance claims for each bar in the histogram. We can then add these values up to get the expected value.

EV = (44% * 0) + (25% * 1) + (15% * 2) + (10% * 3) + (5% * 4) + (1% * 5)
EV = 1.1

We expect an average of <u>1.1 claims per household</u>.

Brainstorming Questions

Brainstorming questions test for two capabilities. One, interviewers want to see that you can structure your thoughts and ideas rather than listing ideas randomly. Two, interviewers want to see that you can think creatively to brainstorm many creative ideas.

The most important aspect of brainstorming questions is to always lay out a simple structure upfront. The structure will not only make you appear intelligent and logical, but it will also help you generate multiple ideas.

A simple structure you can use is an "X" or "Not X" framework. Some examples include the following:

- Economic / non-economic

- Short-term / long-term

- Internal / external

- Quantitative / qualitative

- Revenue-side / cost-side

- Benefits / costs

- Tangible / intangible

These simple two-element frameworks are great because the framework elements are mutually exclusive and completely exhaustive. Each thought or idea that you brainstorm will fit under exactly one element. The two elements collectively should capture all possible ideas.

Brainstorming problem #1: What are the potential barriers to entry for entering the soda market?

Solution to #1: We can think about barriers to entry as economic barriers and non-economic barriers. Economic barriers are requirements needed to enter the market that relate to money or capital. Non-economic barriers are requirements needed to enter the market that are unrelated to money or capital

- Economic
  - Capital
  - Factory space
  - Equipment and machinery

- Non-economic
  - Soda expertise
  - Brand name
  - Distribution channels

Economic barriers include: the capital needed to start the business, factory space to produce soda, and production equipment and machinery.

Non-economic barriers include: expertise in knowing how to produce an outstanding product, brand name to attract customers, and distribution channels to get your product in front of customers.

Brainstorming problem #2: What are the challenges of a fast food restaurant chain entering a new, foreign country?

Solution to #2: We can think of challenges as internal challenges, which are challenges relating to the internal operations of the company, and external challenges, which are challenges not specific to the internal operations of the company.

- Internal
  - Expertise in a new country
  - Understanding a new customer segment
  - Sourcing supplies and labor
  - Setting up the distribution of supplies to restaurants

- External
  - Foreign regulations and compliance
  - Foreign customer perception and reactions
  - Fast food chain competitors

There are two broad types of internal challenges. The first type relates to knowledge or expertise. This includes having the expertise to do business in a foreign country and understanding a new customer segment. The second type of internal challenge relates to logistics. This includes sourcing supplies and labor and setting up distribution.

As for external challenges, we can broadly think of those as challenging relating to the market, customers, and competition. A common market challenge is dealing with regulations and compliance. As for customers, the primary challenge is dealing with their perception and reaction towards businesses. Finally, incumbent competitors will always present a challenge to companies entering a new market.

Brainstorming problem #3: What are the risks of a computer manufacturer, CompU Co., dropping their prices in an attempt to attract and steal customers from competitors?

Solution to #3: We can think about risks in terms of short-term risks, which the computer manufacturer would take on immediately, and long-term risks, which the computer manufacturer may not take on for years after.

- Short-term risks
  - Decline in profits
  - Competitors may also drop prices

- Long-term risks
  - o Brand name or image damage
  - o Difficulty entering the premium computer segment
  - o Loss of suppliers of computer parts

Short-term risks include that CompU Co. could see a decline in overall profits if the increase in sales volume does not offset the decrease in profit per computer sold. Dropping prices could also cause competitors to drop prices. Then, CompU Co. would need to further drop prices in order to take market share from competitors. This cycle of decreasing prices could continue, creating a pricing war that puts pricing pressure on all manufacturers. This would not be good for CompU Co.

Long-term risks include that a decline in prices could negatively impact CompU Co.'s brand name or image if they market themselves as a high-quality or premium computer manufacturer. Additionally, it would be difficult for CompU Co. to later enter the premium, high-priced computer segment if they continue to sell low-priced products. Finally, suppliers of computer parts may not want to work with CompU Co. if they have doubts that they could go out of business due to thin profit margins.

Brainstorming problem #4: Socks Co. makes and sells socks. They have an interesting business model in which they will donate a pair of socks to charity for every pair of socks that they sell. What are the potential benefits of having this business model?

Solution to #4: We can think about benefits as either tangible benefits or intangible benefits. Tangible benefits are benefits that can easily be quantified or measured. Intangible benefits are benefits that can be difficult to quantify or measure.

- Tangible benefits
  - o Increased scale
  - o Higher market share

- Intangible benefits
  - Differentiated value proposition from other socks companies
  - Positive brand image among the public
  - Positive relationships with charities
  - Positive relationships with recipients of the donated socks

The tangible benefits that can be measured are increased production scale and increased market share. Since Socks Co. is giving out a pair of socks for every pair they sell, they effectively double the production quantity of socks needed. This increased scale could drive production costs down per pair of socks. Another tangible benefit is increased market share. In theory, if Socks Co. gives out a pair of socks for every pair they sell, they will have doubled their market share in terms of the number of people that wear their socks.

Intangible benefits include that Socks Co. has a differentiated value proposition from other socks companies because of their social mission. This helps differentiate themselves in the eyes of both investors and consumers. Additionally, Socks Co. will have a positive brand image among the public, which could drive the public to purchase their socks in order to support their social mission. Finally, having positive relationships with charities and recipients of the donated socks means that these people may order more socks later on.

Brainstorming problem #5: What are the potential costs for a city to host an annual technology conference that brings together the most innovative technology companies in the world?

Solution to #5: This should be a fairly straight-forward brainstorming question. We can think about costs as either economic costs or non-economic costs.

- Economic costs
  - Building rent
  - Staff wages
  - Keynote speaker pay
  - Marketing costs

- Non-economic costs
  - Traffic
  - Pollution
  - Crime

Economic costs are costs that can be directly measured by money or capital. These include paying rent for the building that the conference is hosted in, paying the staff wages to run and manage the conference, paying the keynote speakers to come and present, and paying for marketing to raise awareness and interest for the conference.

Non-economic costs are costs that cannot be directly measured by money or capital. These include the increase in traffic congestion in the city, an increase in pollution from having more people in the city, and a potential increase in crime.

Brainstorming problem #6: A real estate developer is trying to get approval from the city's mayor to develop a new port in the city of Bayshore. This port would be used by shipping companies to facilitate the transportation of goods in and out of the city. This would be a massive construction project that would require a substantial number of workers to complete. The construction project would also require a $2M loan. Who are the primary stakeholders that the real estate developer should try to get the approval of?

Solution to #6: We can identify the different stakeholders in this problem by looking at each piece of information we are given.

One potential answer could look like the following:

- City mayor

- Shipping companies

- Labor union

- Financial institution

- Environmental groups

First, we need to consider the city mayor since their approval is necessary to get the new port developed.

Second, we need to consider the shipping companies since they are the ones that will benefit from having a new port. They will be beneficial for supporting the project and helping convince other stakeholders.

Third, since the project requires substantial workers, we need to consider the local labor union and determine how to satisfy them in order to get help from their workers.

Fourth, since the project requires a $2M loan, we need to consider the financial institutions that could help finance this project. Without the loan, this project would not be possible.

Finally, since there is likely to be some ecological harm, we need to consider the environmental groups and how to get them on our side. They are likely to oppose the project and will try to convince the mayor and other stakeholders that the project should be abandoned.

Brainstorming problem #7: Ballers Co. is a company that produces basketball shoes. What are potential adjacent markets for them to enter?

Solution to #7: We can structure all of the potential adjacent markets by how far they are from the core basketball shoe market.

- Basketball-adjacent markets
  - Basketball socks
  - Basketball shorts and pants
  - Basketball tops and jackets
  - Basketball accessories

- Shoe-adjacent markets
  - Volleyball shoes
  - Running shoes
  - Football shoes
  - Soccer shoes
  - Tennis shoes

- Sports consumer retail market
    - Volleyball apparel and accessories
    - Running apparel and accessories
    - Football apparel and accessories
    - Soccer apparel and accessories
    - Tennis apparel and accessories

- Sports consumer non-retail market
    - Sports private or group lessons
    - Sports equipment repair
    - Sports tournaments or leagues
    - Professional sports teams

The closest adjacent markets are those related to basketball. Ballers Co. could sell basketball socks, shorts, pants, tops, jackets, and accessories in addition to selling basketball shoes.

The next closest adjacent markets are those related to shoes. Ballers Co. could sell shoes in other sports, such as volleyball, running, football, soccer, and tennis.

Following this, the next closest adjacent markets relate to the sports consumer retail sector in general. Ballers Co. could sell apparel and accessories in other sports besides basketball.

Finally, the furthest adjacent markets relate to the non-retail sector of the sports consumer market. Ballers Co. could offer private or group lessons for sports, offer sports equipment repair, host sports tournaments or leagues, or own and manage a professional sports team. Because these markets are so far from Ballers Co.'s core market, basketball shoes, they are unlikely to happen in the short-term.

The adjacent markets that make the most sense to enter are either basketball-adjacent markets or shoe-adjacent markets.

Brainstorming problem #8: How can a movie theater increase revenues?

Solution to #8: We can think about ways to increase revenues either through organic growth or inorganic growth. Organic growth is growth done through the company's own operations while inorganic growth is growth through acquisition. Within organic growth, we can think of growth through existing revenue streams and growth through new revenue streams.

- Organic growth
  - Growth through existing revenue streams
    - Increase the price of movie tickets, concessions, or merchandise sold
    - Increase the volume of movie tickets, concessions, or merchandise sold through marketing
  - Growth through new revenue streams
    - Sell meals during movies
    - Offer premium comfort seats for purchase
    - Offer seating in premium theaters with higher quality screens and sound systems for purchase
    - Show television shows, sports games, or older movies during low occupancy hours

- Inorganic growth
  - Acquire another movie theater
  - Acquire an empty parking lot to show movies outdoors

Looking at organic growth through existing revenue streams, we can increase price or increase volume in order to grow revenues. Looking at organic growth through new revenue streams, we can brainstorm additional offerings that the movie theater could provide. These include selling meals, offering premium comfort seating or a premium theater screen, or showing things besides movies.

Looking at inorganic growth, the movie theater could acquire another movie theater or they could acquire an empty parking lot to show movies outdoors. Brainstorming ideas like the latter helps demonstrate your creativity to the interviewer.

Brainstorming problem #9: Our client is looking to sell enterprise software to businesses to help their sales employees better manage customer relationships. What are some different pricing options we can offer?

Solution to #9: We can think about pricing options as either offering a flat price independent of usage or offering variable pricing that depends on usage.

- Flat pricing
    - One-time purchase
    - Monthly or annual subscription

- Variable pricing
    - Price per number of employee licenses
    - Price per number of customers managed
    - Price per frequency of use
    - Price as a percentage of employee sales made

Looking at flat pricing, the enterprise software could be priced as a one-time purchase to companies, giving them unlimited and unrestricted use. Alternatively, the software could be priced as a monthly or annual subscription. Once the company stops their subscription, they will no longer have access to the software.

Looking at variable pricing, we could sell the software based on the number of employees that would be using the software. We could also price the software based on the number of customers that are managed within the software. Thirdly, we can price the software based on the frequency of use, whether that is by the number of times the software is opened or by the number of hours users use the software. Finally, we could price the software as a percentage of sales that users make. This would be a form of profit-sharing between the software company and the company that purchases the software.

Brainstorming problem #10: A New York bagel shop has been selling $1 bagels over the past twenty years. Costs of the raw materials needed to make the bagels continue to rise, but the price of the bagels has not changed. How can the bagel shop continue to sell their bagels for $1?

Solution to #10: We can brainstorm potential ideas as either cost strategies or revenue strategies.

- Cost strategies
    - Switch to cheaper substitute ingredients
    - Make bagels smaller
    - Switch to using cheaper labor
    - Increase scale to decrease costs of raw materials
    - Switch to a location with lower rent
    - Reduce operating hours

- Revenue strategies
    - Increase the prices of other goods sold
    - Sell more higher margin goods
    - Require a minimum order quantity

Cost strategies include finding ways to decrease variable costs despite an increase in costs of raw materials. This can be done by switching to cheaper substitute ingredients, using less raw ingredients to make bagels smaller, switching to cheaper labor, or increasing scale in order to decrease costs of raw materials. Fixed costs can also be reduced by switching to a location with lower rent or reducing operating hours.

Revenue strategies include increasing the prices of other goods sold that customers typically purchase bundled with their bagels. These goods may include coffee or juice. The bagel shop could also be driving a change in sales mix by selling higher margin goods rather than focusing on selling lower margin bagels. Finally, the bagel shop could impose a minimum order quantity to increase the volume of bagels sold. This could make up for lower bagel margins.

Brainstorming problem #11: How can a trucking transportation company that delivers produce from farms to supermarkets reduce costs?

Solution to #11: We can think about ways to reduce costs as either reducing fixed costs or reducing variable costs.

- Reducing fixed costs
  o Renegotiate wages for truck drivers
  o Refinance leases for trucks
  o Switch to trucks that are more durable

- Reducing variable costs
  o Use cheaper gas
  o Decrease the number of trips
  o Optimize truck routes

Fixed costs are typically more difficult to reduce. Strategies include renegotiating wages for truck drivers to decrease wages paid, refinancing leases for trucks to lower interest payments, and switching to trucks that last longer, decreasing the number of trucks needed over a period of time.

Reducing variable costs is much easier to implement. Strategies include using cheaper gas to fuel trucks, transporting produce only when trucks are fully loaded to decrease the number of trips taken, and optimizing produce pickup and delivery routes.

Brainstorming problem #12: What are the potential reasons why a private equity firm would buy a company that is not profitable?

Solution to #12: In this problem, we can also think about potential reasons as short-term reasons and long-term reasons.

- Short-term reasons
  o Diversify existing portfolio
  o Dismantle company and sell parts
  o Acquire competitor of an existing portfolio company
  o Synergies

- Long-term reasons
  o Turn around and resell the company
  o Hedge for future market shifts

One potential short-term reason is that the private equity firm is trying to diversify their portfolio. The acquired company may not be profitable now, but perhaps it will be profitable in market conditions in which the private equity firm's portfolio companies are not profitable. A second short-term reason is that the private equity firm could be looking to dismantle the company and sell individual components to buyers. A third reason is that the private equity firm may be trying to remove a competitor in a market where one of their portfolio companies plays. Finally, there could be revenue or cost synergies that can be realized from this acquisition.

One potential long-term reason is that the private equity firm may be looking to turn around the acquired company and resell the company years later for a meaningful return on investment. Additionally, the private equity firm could be looking to hedge for future market shifts. Perhaps the acquired company is unprofitable now, but could be highly successful when the market evolves and changes.

Brainstorming problem #13: What are the different ways a traditional oil & gas utility company could enter the clean energy (e.g., solar energy, turbine energy) market?

Solution to #13: There are typically three different ways a company can enter a new market: develop capabilities internally, enter a partnership or joint venture, or acquire an existing player.

- Develop capabilities internally
  - Invest in clean energy research and development
  - Hire clean energy employees from other companies

- Enter a partnership or joint venture
  - Partner with an existing player to get access to their technology
  - Form a joint venture with an existing player to co-invest in servicing a market

- Make an acquisition
  - Acquire a solar panel or turbine manufacturer
  - Acquire an existing clean energy provider

In order to develop capabilities internally, the oil & gas utilities company would need to invest in clean energy research and development. They could also hire clean energy employees from other companies to speed up this process up since these employees already have some expertise in the space.

When considering entering a partnership or joint venture, the oil & gas utility company could partner with an existing player to get access to their technology. In exchange, the oil & gas utilities company could offer their distribution channels or customer base. An alternative option is to form a joint venture with an existing player. The oil & gas utilities company would provide part of the investment or funding needed to service a market in exchange for sharing a portion of profits.

When considering making an acquisition, the oil & gas utility company could acquire a company that manufactures solar panels or turbines to gain full control and access to their technology. They could also acquire an existing clean energy provider to acquire their brand name, customer base, and employees.

Brainstorming problem #14: What are the different reasons why a TV cable company would acquire an online, on-demand streaming company?

Solution to #14: We can think about the different reasons for making this acquisition as short-term reasons and long-term reasons.

- Short-term reasons
  - Drive growth
  - Eliminate a competitor
  - Revenue synergies
  - Cost synergies

- Long-term reasons
  - Hedge for future market shifts
  - Enter the on-demand streaming market
  - Expand offerings

One short-reason could be to drive growth. The TV cable market is a fairly mature market with flat or declining growth, so an acquisition could be one of the few ways to grow the company. Another short-term reason could be to eliminate a competitor that is taking customers away from cable TV. A third short-term reason is for revenue synergies. Perhaps the TV cable company can cross-sell on-demand streaming to their existing customers or vice-versa. A fourth reason is for cost synergies. With increased scale and reach, perhaps the TV cable company can reduce their costs.

One long-term reason could be to hedge for future market shifts. Perhaps in the future, all customers will be streaming content online instead of watching cable TV. Without this acquisition, the cable TV company would be out of business. Another reason is that perhaps the cable TV company wants to enter the on-demand streaming market and is using this acquisition to get a head start. Finally, perhaps the cable TV company wants to expand their suite of offerings beyond cable TV. Making this acquisition would add another offering to their suite of products.

Business Judgment Questions

Business judgment questions will ask you to take a stance on a business issue or ask for your opinion on a business question. Most of the time, you won't have much information or data to work with besides your own business acumen.

The purpose of these types of questions is to: (1) assess your business acumen and (2) determine if you can communicate your thoughts in a clear and structured way.

In a way, these types of questions are very similar to brainstorming questions. However, once you have brainstormed your ideas, you will need to take it a step further by taking a concrete stance or forming an opinion on the business issue or question.

For these types of questions, it is acceptable to ask the interviewer for a minute so that you can gather and structure your thoughts. A simple, but effective structure you can take is the following:

"I believe [state your position or stance]. There are two reasons that support this. One... Two..."

As you take the time to brainstorm, try to list arguments or reasons for both sides of the issue. Then, pick the stance or side of the issue that you were able to list the greatest number of reasons for.

The key to doing well on these types of questions is to make sure you have two or three reasons that back up your position or stance. Having strong, logical supporting reasons is much more important than which side of the issue you take.

Business judgment problem #1: A luxury fashion retailer sells high-end women's purses and wallets. For the upcoming holiday season, they are considering running a promotion in which they would discount their purses by 30%. Based on your business intuition, do you think this marketing strategy makes sense?

Solution to #1: Remember that it does not matter what stance you take on this question, as long as your reasons are logical and make sense. In this problem, it may be easier to take the stance that the luxury fashion retailer should not offer a promotion since luxury goods are typically not discounted because the high price is an indication of luxury. A potential answer could look like the following:

"I don't think that the luxury fashion retailer should offer a holiday promotion for three reasons.

One, offering a 30% discount goes against the company's brand image of luxury and premiumness. If the company prices their products at a discount, some customers may perceive that as a decline in quality or luxury. Therefore, this could hurt the company's brand image in the long-run.

Two, by running a holiday sale, the company may be setting expectations among customers that there will be a holiday sale next year as well. This may cause customers to hold out on making a purchase until the holiday season, when they would expect a discount promotion.

Three, we are unsure of whether this promotion would actually increase profits. Since the company is selling purses at a discount, they need to sell a higher volume of purses to make up for the decrease in profit margin for each purse sold. Unless we know for sure that volume would increase meaningfully, it is better not to take the risk of running this promotion."

Business judgment problem #2: The smartphone apps market is a very fragmented market with hundreds of thousands of developers creating nearly a million different apps that are available for download. A company that produces computer video games is trying to enter the smartphone video game apps market. What do you think is the best way to enter the market? Should they build up capabilities internally or make an acquisition?

Solution to #2: Again, it does not matter what stance you take on this question as long as you have logical reasons that make sense. For this problem, it may be easier to take the stance that the computer video game company should build up capabilities internally since the smartphone video game apps market is highly fragmented and there is potentially a lot of overlap with existing capabilities. One potential answer could look like the following:

"I believe that the computer video game company should build up capabilities internally to enter the smartphone video game apps market. I have three reasons for this.

One, the smartphone apps market is highly fragmented. This implies that there are low barriers to entry. Therefore, the company should be able to enter the market relatively easily without making a costly acquisition.

Two, there is likely significant overlap with existing capabilities. Video game ideation and design are likely similar between the two markets. Therefore, the company should be able to leverage a lot of their existing capabilities.

Three, instead of making an acquisition, the company could simply hire new employees that have experience producing smartphone video game apps. This would be much cheaper than making an acquisition. This would also fill any capability gaps the company may have."

Business judgment problem #3: Thayer is a pharmaceutical and consumer packaged goods company that develops drugs and also produces consumer health goods, such as skin and beauty products. They are considering selling their consumer health goods online. How can they compete with Omazon, a massive online retailer that has a wider variety of consumer health goods, many at lower prices, and with free two-day shipping?

Solution to #3: The key to this problem is recognizing that Thayer will not be able to compete with Omazon on price, product variety, and likely shipping. However, Thayer can leverage capabilities that Omazon does not have. Since Thayer is a pharmaceutical company, they have access to physician and patient data. One potential answer could look like the following:

"There are three different ways that Thayer can compete with Omazon.

One, they can leverage their brand name as a company that sells consumer health goods that physicians and patients approve of. Since Omazon is not a pharmaceutical company, they cannot use this strategy to sell their products.

Two, Thayer can leverage their relationships with physicians to push their products. Patients typically trust their doctors and are likely to purchase specific products that they recommend.

Three, Thayer can leverage patient data to create superior consumer health products. They can then position their products as premium products and sell them at a higher price-point than Omazon. This way, Thayer does not compete in the same market as Omazon."

Business judgment problem #4: Your client operates thousands of gas stations across the US that sell gasoline to customers to fuel their vehicles. Gasoline is a highly commoditized product. Customers cannot tell the difference between gasoline from one gas station and gasoline from another gas station. They typically purchase gasoline from the gas station that has the lowest price. In this type of competitive market, how can your client grow?

Solution to #4: To grow in this type of environment, the company needs to determine a way to differentiate itself from competitors. Even though gas is a commoditized product, they can still differentiate on the other services or amenities that gas stations provide. One potential answer could look like the following:

"In order to grow, I think our client should identify ways to differentiate themselves from competitors on the services or amenities that gas stations provide. I have three potential ideas.

One, our client can try to position their gas stations as convenient and time-saving. They can install payment mechanisms that allow customers to purchase more quickly. They can also install pumps that deliver gas quicker.

Two, our client can try to position their gas stations as a premium service. They can offer gas station attendants that fill up your car with gas for you. They can also provide high-quality snacks or drinks to customers or provide very clean bathrooms for use.

Three, our client can try to attach popular fast food restaurants to their gas stations to differentiate themselves on food offerings. This way, customers will associate the company's gas stations with a place to grab a familiar meal."

Business judgment problem #5: You have created a new type of shower that is vastly superior to existing showers. This new type of shower has better temperature control, pressure control, and conserves more water. Customers that are looking to install or replace their shower system typically hire plumbers to choose and install a shower. Plumbers are the ones typically knowledgeable in the different shower installation options. 80% of the plumbing companies in the country are small businesses with one to four employees. What do you think is the biggest challenge of selling this product?

Solution to #5: In this problem, it is clear that this new type of shower is superior to existing showers. However, what makes this market complicated is that plumbers are the ones that choose what shower to install. Even if the end consumer wants to have this new type of shower, the plumbers need to be incentivized to install this shower and know how to install it. A potential answer could look like the following:

"I believe that the biggest challenge of selling this product is getting distribution. There are three reasons for this.

One, plumbers are not incentivized to recommend installing this shower to customers. Plumbers likely already have a list of shower systems that they typically recommend and know how to install. There is nothing to incentivize them to learn how to install a new shower system.

Two, educating plumbers on this new shower system will be challenging because of how fragmented the plumbing services market is. Since 80% of plumbing companies are small businesses with one to four employees, it will take significant time and effort to educate all of the plumbers.

Three, the need to replace or install a new shower is very infrequent. Customers may replace or install showers perhaps once every ten years. Therefore, getting word of mouth referrals from customers will take a long time."

Business judgment problem #6: Your client sells innovative, high-technology devices, such as virtual reality headsets. They frequently experience inventory problems in which they either run out of product to sell or have too much inventory that they cannot sell off. Between these two different types of inventory problems, which do you think is a larger problem to have?

Solution to #6: You could make compelling reasons for either side. I'll provide both sides of the argument below.

If you believe that running out of product is a larger problem, one answer could look like the following:

"I believe running out of product to sell is a larger problem for three reasons.

One, running out of product results in unhappy, unsatisfied customers. If a customer is not able to purchase a product, they may be unhappy and choose not to buy from your company.

Two, running out of product gives competitors an opportunity to meet and satisfy your own customers' demand. Therefore, by not having sufficient inventory, you are giving up sales and market share to competitors.

Three, by the time you restock your inventory, customer needs and preferences may have already changed. Perhaps there will be newer technologies that customers want to buy and they may no longer have an interest in your product."

If you believe that having too much inventory is a larger problem, one answer could look like the following:

"I believe having too much inventory is a larger problem for three reasons.

One, unsold product that sits in inventory has holding costs, which can be quite expensive. These holding costs can eat away into profit and lower the product's profit margin.

Two, if inventory is held for too long, then the product could become obsolete. For example, if newer technology comes out, then older technology products may no longer be desirable and customers may no longer want to purchase your obsolete product.

Three, having inventory ties up working capital. Instead of spending money to produce products that sit in inventory, that money could have been invested or used elsewhere in the company. In other words, the money spent on producing the unsold products could have been put to better use."

Business judgment problem #7: Hardcore Snacks produces and sells beef jerky targeted towards middle-aged men that value authentic, bold, and full-flavored jerky. In response to a growing millennial age segment that values health-conscious foods, Hardcore Snacks wants to launch a less tasty, but healthier line of turkey jerky to cater towards this new segment. How should Hardcore Snacks go about launching this new healthy snack line?

Solution to #7: The key problem you want to avoid is losing your existing customers because you have created a new product that does not fit with the company's overall brand name and values.

Therefore, when launching this new healthy snack line, the company should make every effort to keep these two different products as separated as possible. One potential answer could look like the following:

"Hardcore Snacks should launch their new healthy turkey jerky product line as a separate brand name. There are three reasons that support this.

One, having a separate brand name for their healthy jerky will allow the company to position and brand their new product towards an entirely new customer segment. They will not be restricted or confined by their already established brand name in Hardcore Snacks.

Two, having a separate brand name for their healthy snacks will prevent alienating their existing customers. Since their healthy snacks are under a new brand name, loyalists to Hardcore Snacks should not think that the Hardcore Snacks brand is deteriorating or shifting towards a different value proposition.

Three, launching a separate brand for their new product protects Hardcore Snacks' brand name in case the new product fails."

Business judgment problem #8: Your client is an enterprise software company that sells software packages in three different markets: data backup and recovery, data transfer, and data security. The data backup and recovery market accounts for 70% of their revenues and the market is growing at 1% per year. Data transfer accounts for 20% of their revenues and this market is declining at 8% per year. Data security accounts for 10% of the company's revenues and this market is growing at 12% per year. What should your client's strategy for growth be?

Solution to #8: In this problem, we have three markets that are in entirely different maturity stages. Data backup and recovery is likely a mature market since it is growing at 1% per year. Data transfer is likely an old, dying market since it is declining at 8% per year. Data security is likely a new, emerging market since it is growing quickly at 12% per year. We should have different strategies for each of these three different markets. One potential answer could look like the following:

"Our client should approach their three different markets with three different strategies.

For data backup and recovery, the company should continue making substantial investments to maintain and grow market share since this segment accounts for 70% of revenues.

For data transfer, the company should significantly reduce investments since this market is declining. They should only make the minimum investments needed to keep this segment up and running as long as the segment is still profitable. Once this segment becomes unprofitable, the company should exit this segment entirely.

For data security, the company should begin increasing investments and funding in this space. Although this segment is small now, it has the potential to become very big because of the high growth rate."

"Why Consulting?" & "Why This Firm?" Questions

There are two questions you are almost certainly going to be asked at some point during your consulting interview.

1. Why do you want to do consulting?

2. Why do you want to work at this firm?

Make sure you have prepared answers to both of these questions before your consulting interview.

Looking at the first question, there are a variety of different reasons you could give. I recommend having at least three reasons why you want to go into consulting.

I recommend using the following simple, but effective structure when answering this question:

"Consulting is currently my top career choice for the following three reasons. One… Two… Three… At this moment, I feel that no other career better suits my professional needs and goals than consulting."

Reasons you could give for "why consulting?" include the following:

- I am looking to make a significant impact by working with top executives at billion-dollar companies on their most challenging business problems

- I enjoy the diversity and novelty of solving business problems and challenges across multiple different industries and functions

- I see consulting as the quickest way to build a strong toolkit, both on hard skills and soft skills, to become a business executive

- I see consulting as the quickest way to build a strong toolkit, both on hard skills and soft skills, to found a company

- I enjoy working closely with small teams on tough, challenging business problems

- I want to get an insider view on how large companies are run and operated

- I want to develop knowledge and expertise in a particular industry or function

- The opportunity to work across multiple different industries and functions will help narrow down my interests and help me decide on my future career path

- I value the significant mentorship and personal development that consulting provides

- Consulting provides an opportunity to learn how to manage others at a relatively early stage in my career

- I find excitement in working with and servicing clients, helping deliver significant value to them

- I am excited to travel to different places around the world for work

- I don't have a business background and feel consulting is the best opportunity for me to transition into the business side of companies

Whichever reasons you have for consulting, make sure they are appropriate and genuine. Interviewers can tell when a candidate is blindly listing reasons for going into consulting and not demonstrating real passion and interest for consulting.

Looking at the second question, there are also a variety of different reasons you could give. Again, I recommend having at least three reasons why you want to work at a particular consulting firm.

I recommend using the following simple, but effective structure when answering this question:

"[Firm name] is a top choice for me for three reasons. One... Two... Three... I would absolutely love to work for [firm name]."

Reasons you could give for "why this firm?" include the following:

- I've really loved the people that I've met from [firm name] and would enjoy working with them

- [Firm name] has an amazing culture that is both hard-working, but fun. I would love to be a part of that culture and environment

- [Firm name] has deep expertise in a particular industry or function, which I am very passionate about

- [Firm name] has a strong presence in a particular country, which I am interested in working in later in my career

- [Firm name] places a heavy investment in mentorship and personal development, which I value tremendously

- I am really excited about a particular program or opportunity that [firm name] offers

- [Firm name] has a local staffing model and I appreciate getting to know my colleagues on a deeper level

- [Firm name] has a global staffing model and I appreciate the opportunity to work in different countries and get to know many different people around the world

- Several of my mentors that I respect and look up to have worked at [firm name]. They have highly recommended working here

Again, whichever reasons you pick for why you want to work at a particular firm, make sure they are genuine and appropriate.

Behavioral Questions

Behavioral questions ask you to draw upon a time or experience in the past in which you demonstrated a particular skill, trait, or dealt with a particular kind of adversity. Examples of behavioral questions include the following:

- Tell me about a time when you were able to successfully persuade someone

- Give a time when you had to use data to solve a problem

- Describe a situation in which you failed. How did you react to it?

- Tell me about your proudest accomplishment

- Describe a situation in which you faced conflict while working on a team. How did you handle that?

The behavioral questions you get asked during a consulting interview are just like the behavioral questions you may get asked in any other interview. However, since most of the time spent during a consulting interview is on solving a case, you'll likely get asked no more than a few behavioral questions in each interview round.

Behavioral questions assess a couple of different things. First, it tries to use past behavior to determine future performance or success. Since candidates are asked to describe actual past behavior, interviewers get a sense of what it would be like to work with the candidate.

Second, behavioral questions assess how well a candidate can communicate or articulate a story. Does the candidate explain things clearly and effectively? Does the candidate keep their stories concise?

Third, behavioral questions give the interviewer a sense of the candidate's personality and cultural fit with the firm. Does the candidate appear confident or timid? Is the candidate enthusiastic or dull? How a candidate responds to a behavioral question also gives a lot of insight into the values and morals that a candidate believes in.

There are potentially hundreds of different behavioral questions you could get asked. Rather than preparing answers for each of these questions individually, I recommend an alternative approach that is much more efficient, but still effective.

Prepare 4-8 different stories based on your past experiences, both from professional and personal experiences. You want to select stories that are your most impressive or impactful experiences. Additionally, you want to ensure that your stories are collectively diverse. You don't want to have five stories all about leadership. Instead, perhaps have one story on leadership, one on dealing with conflict, one on dealing with failure, one on mentoring, etc.

When you get asked a behavioral question, mentally run through your prepared list of stories and select the story that is most relevant. Adapt your story or reframe it if necessary to ensure that it is tailored to the specific behavioral question.

When you get asked another behavioral question, mentally run through your prepared list of stories that you have not shared yet and repeat the same process.

This method ensures that your mind will not go blank during an interview. You will always have a story that you can share with the interviewer. Additionally, this method ensures that you are sharing only the most impressive and impactful stories that best highlight your traits and accomplishments since you have prepared your stories beforehand.

When answering behavioral questions, make sure you tell your story in a structured way. This not only helps keep your stories concise, but helps you to focus on the key message that you want to deliver to the interviewer. One simple, but effective structure to use is the STAR method, which stands for Situation, Task, Action, and Result. When telling a story, go through each of the following points.

Situation: Provide brief context and overview of the situation you were in. When was this? Where were you? Who was involved? Try to keep this section concise because the interviewer cares most about the Action and Result sections.

Task: Describe what you were asked or required to deliver or achieve. In other words, what were the goals and objectives that you had to meet? Again, try to keep this section concise to give yourself more time to go through the Action and Result sections.

Action: What did you do? In other words, what actions or steps did you take in order to handle the task or meet the objectives?

Result: Describe the outcome and what impact your actions had. Were you able to meet the goals or objectives that you mentioned in the Task section? What did you learn from this experience? How did this experience help you grow and develop?

Now that you have a strategy for preparing for behavioral questions and answering them, make sure to take the time to practice. Behavioral questions should be easy because you know what types of questions you will be asked and you have the opportunity to pre-rehearse them beforehand.

I've included 20 behavioral questions below. This is not meant to be a comprehensive list of behavioral questions, but this list should give you an idea of the types of questions you could get asked.

Teamwork Questions

- Describe a time when you had to make an individual sacrifice for the good of the team

- Tell me about a time when you worked on a highly effective team. What made the team so successful?

- What is the typical role that you take when working on a team?

Leadership Questions

- Give an example of a time when you had to lead a team or group

- Describe a situation in which you had to motivate someone

- Tell me about a time you showed initiative

- Give me an example of a time when you went above and beyond the call of duty

- Tell me about a time when you had to be flexible and adaptable

Conflict Questions

- Tell me about a situation in which you had to deal with someone difficult to work with

- Describe a time you had a disagreement with a teammate

- Tell me about a time when you had to persuade someone on a particular course of action

Problem Solving Questions

- Give a time when you had to use data to solve a problem

- Describe a difficult or complicated problem that you faced. How did you approach the problem?

- Tell me about a time when you had to make a decision, but did not have all of the information you needed

- Describe a time when you had too many things to do. How did you handle this?

Failure Questions

- Give an example of a time when you tried to accomplish something, but failed

- Describe a situation in which you made a mistake. What did you do about it?

- Tell me about a time you failed to meet a deadline. What things did you do to fail? What did you learn?

Accomplishment Questions

- What accomplishment are you most proud of?

- What accomplishment has been the most rewarding for you?

- What is an accomplishment that you are proud of that is not on your resume?

Strengths and Weaknesses Questions

- What is your greatest strength?

- What is a piece of feedback you have received from a former supervisor or colleague?

- Why should we hire you?

Part II: Practice Cases

Introduction to Practice Cases

Case interviews are best done with a case interview partner. Your case interview partner will take on the role of an interviewer and will be leading you through the case interview, providing case information to you, and questioning your answers and approaches. Typically, after completing one case, you will switch roles with your partner and you will give your partner a case, taking on the role of an interviewer.

I cannot stress how much more valuable it is to practice case interviews with a partner rather than by yourself. Practicing with a partner more closely simulates the actual interview, forcing you to interact and collaborate with the interviewer to get to a recommendation.

Because not everyone can find a case interview partner, I have written the following practice cases in a way that they can be done individually.

Before jumping into the practice cases, I'll quickly go through how to best conduct practice cases.

Best practices for being the interviewer

1. Make sure to read the entire case and know all of the information.

2. Decide if you want this case to be an interviewer-led or candidate-led interview.

   Interviewer-led case: You will be guiding the candidate through the case. Ask the candidate the case questions in the order that they appear.

   Candidate-led case: Ask the candidate to decide where they want to start the case. Provide information only if specifically asked for. If the candidate is going down a path that is not essential for solving the case, tell the candidate that there is no further information on that topic. If the candidate is stuck, you may have to proactively help nudge the candidate in the right direction.

3. Decide what tone or personality type you want to take on as the interviewer.

   Taking on different interview styles will help the candidate work with and adjust to different types of interviewers. Some different styles include:

   Positive and helpful: Be collaborative and supportive of the candidate. Encourage the candidate if they are struggling and compliment the candidate when they provide a good answer.

   Cold and aloof: Pretend to not take an interest in the candidate and what they have to say. Do not give away whether you think the candidate is providing a good or poor answer. Answer questions curtly.

   Challenging and contentious: Ask questions and challenge the approaches or answers that the candidate presents. Ask why they chose to make certain conclusions and whether or not they have considered other factors. State your own opinions and thoughts to see how the candidate reacts.

4. Immediately after completing the case, make sure to provide specific and thorough feedback on the candidate's

114

performance. It is important to do this as soon as possible because the candidate's performance will be freshest in your mind.

Best practices for being the candidate

1. Ask clarifying questions when you are unclear or unsure about something. Especially make sure that you understand the case objective.

2. When developing an initial framework for solving the case, ask the interviewer for a couple of minutes to structure your thoughts.

3. After walking the interviewer through your initial framework, be prepared to suggest an area to investigate or discuss first.

4. When doing the math, make sure to talk out loud what you are doing and walk the interviewer through your work and thought process.

5. If the math is somewhat complicated, make sure to set up a structure or framework before diving into the nitty-gritty math calculations.

6. Try to structure your answer to every qualitative business question that you get asked.

7. When presenting your final conclusion, state your recommendation first. Then talk through the two or three reasons that support your recommendation. Finally, discuss what potential next steps could be.

Best practices for doing practice cases individually

1. Make sure you practice presenting your framework and answers out loud. Imagine that there is an interviewer in the room that you are speaking to.

2. Only look at the sample answers after you have fully developed and presented your own answer.

3. Do not give yourself unlimited time to think of an answer to each question. Imagine that there is an interviewer in the room that will grow impatient if you are taking too much time

4. Put away any calculators, notes, or other materials. In a real case interview, you will not have access to these. To get the most out of doing practice cases, you want to simulate a real case interview as closely as possible.

5. Do not take breaks during a practice case. Finish the entire case from start to end. In a real case interview, you will not get the opportunity to take a break.

Additional cases

HackingTheCaseInterview.com has 15 additional challenging practice cases with detailed solutions.

Practice Case #1 - Aquador

Difficulty: Easy

Our client, Aquador, is a large bottled beverage producer with annual revenues of $2B. They sell a variety of consumer beverages such as sodas, juices, and sports drinks in the US.

Due to a recent consumer health trend focused on reducing consumption of sugar, they are considering entering the zero-calorie, flavored water beverage market. Should they enter this market?

(Sample framework is on the following page)

<u>Sample Framework</u>: One potential framework could look like the following. The candidate does not need to have this exact framework, but should capture many of these points.

- Flavored water beverage market attractiveness
    - What is the market size?
    - What is the market growth rate?
    - What are the average profit margins?

- Competitive landscape
    - How many players are there?
    - How much share does each player have?
    - Are competitors differentiated or do they have any competitive advantage?

- Aquador's capabilities
    - Does Aquador have the expertise to create an outstanding flavored water beverage?
    - Does Aquador have the production capabilities to produce flavored water beverages at scale?
    - Are there any existing synergies that Aquador could leverage?

- Expected profitability?
    - What are the expected revenues?
    - What are the expected costs?
    - How long would it take to break even on their initial investment to enter the market?

<u>Question 1</u>: Estimate the market size of flavored water beverages in the US.

(Sample answer is on the following page)

<u>Answer to Question 1</u>: One potential structure for this market sizing problem could look like the following:

- Start with the US population

- Estimate what percentage would drink flavored water beverages

- Segment customers as light, medium, and heavy drinkers

- Estimate the number of bottles consumed per year

- Estimate the average selling price per bottle

- Multiply these figures to determine the market size

We'll assume that the US population is roughly 320M people. We estimate that perhaps 50% of the population would drink a flavored water beverage. That gives us 320M * 50% = 160M potential customers.

Among these customers, we may estimate that 25% are light drinkers, 50% are medium drinkers, and 25% are heavy drinkers. That means, we have 40M light drinkers, 80M medium drinkers, and 40M heavy drinkers.

Let's estimate that light drinkers will drink one bottle every week. If we assume roughly 50 weeks a year, that means they drink 50 bottles per year. For medium drinkers, assume they drink two bottles per week or roughly 100 bottles per year. Finally, for heavy drinkers, assume they drink 5 bottles per week or roughly 250 bottles per year.

We can now calculate the total number of bottles consumed per year. (40M * 50) + (80M * 100) + (40M * 250) = 2B + 8B + 10B = 20B bottles consumed per year.

Next, let's estimate that the average cost per bottle of flavored water is $1. Therefore, 20B bottles *$1 per bottle = $20B.

The market size for flavored water beverages is $20B in the US. This is a large market, ten times the size of Aquador's annual revenue.

Question 2: Assume that from the previous problem, you determined that the market size for flavored water in the US is $20B. Based on the following chart, what conclusions can you draw about the market?

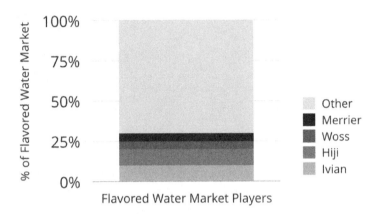

(Sample answer is on the following page)

<u>Answer to Question 2</u>: The key takeaway is that the market is highly fragmented. The market leader only has roughly 10% market share. The top four players only have about 30% market share collectively. Therefore, the rest of the 70% of the market is composed of many small players that have less than about 5% market share each.

Since the market is fragmented, this implies that there are low barriers to entry in this market. Therefore, it looks promising for Aquador to enter the flavored water beverage market.

Question 3: What are some synergies that Aquador can leverage with their existing business if they were to enter the flavored water beverage market?

(Sample answer is on the following page)

<u>Answer to Question 3</u>: We can think about potential synergies as revenue synergies and cost synergies.

- Revenue synergies
  - Distribution channels
  - Aquador brand name
  - Cross-selling with existing customers

- Cost synergies
  - Supply of water used for other beverages
  - Supply of fruits to flavor the water
  - Production equipment
  - Bottling plants
  - Transportation vehicles
  - Sales and marketing team

Revenue synergies include leveraging existing distribution channels to get the new flavored water beverage in front of customers, Aquador's brand name for marketing purposes, and cross-selling to existing customers.

Cost synergies include using the existing supplies of water and fruits that are used to produce Aquador's existing beverages. Aquador could probably also use the same production equipment, bottling plants, transportation vehicles, and the same sales and marketing team.

<u>Question 4</u>: Setting up a facility in one of Aquador's plants to produce and bottle a flavored water beverage would cost roughly $400M. Aquador would sell their bottles for $1 each. It costs $0.75 to produce and ship each bottle. How many bottles would Aquador need to sell each year in order to break even within 5 years?

Is this breakeven point feasible? Aquador believes that they can capture at least a 2% market share. Assume that the flavored water beverage market size is 20B bottles.

(Sample answer is on the following page)

Answer to Question 4: Let x = the total number of bottles sold over 5 years. We can set up an equation to determine the number of bottles that need to be sold in order to break even on the $400M investment.

$$x * (\$1 - \$0.75) = \$400M$$
$$x = 1.6B$$

Aquador needs to sell 1.6B bottles over 5 years. This means that they need to sell 1.6B / 5 = 320M bottles per year.

We can now calculate what market share this represents.

Market share = (320M * $1) / $20B = 1.6%

Aquador would need to capture a 1.6% market share in order to break even and they believe they will capture at least a 2% market share. This breakeven point seems feasible.

At this point, you could have also made the conclusion that if Aquador captures 2% market share, they would increase revenues by 2% * $20B = $400M. They currently have $2B in annual revenues, so this would increase their revenues by 20%.

<u>Conclusion</u>: The CEO of Aquador asks for your recommendation. Should they enter the flavored water beverage market?

(Sample conclusion is on the following page)

<u>Sample Conclusion</u>: One potential recommendation is presented below.

"I believe that Aquador should enter the flavored water beverage market for the following three reasons.

One, the market size for flavored water beverages is $20B and we expect to capture at least a 2% market share. This would increase Aquador's revenues by $400M, an increase of 25% over their current annual revenues of $2B.

Two, the market is highly fragmented with the top four players only having 30% market share. This implies low barriers to entry, making market entry attractive.

Three, there are many synergies that Aquador could leverage when producing flavored water beverages. On the revenue side, they can leverage existing distribution channels, Aquador's brand name, and cross-selling. On the cost side, they can leverage their bottling plants, production equipment, supply of water and fruits, and their sales and marketing team.

For next steps, I'd like to look into two areas. One, I'd look into the potential risks of entering the market and what steps can be taken to mitigate them. Two, I'd look into how Aquador should position or market their product to customers."

Practice Case #2 – Swift Enterprises

Difficulty: Easy

Swift Enterprises manufactures and sells jet skis to consumers for recreational use. Swift Enterprises has been experiencing a decline in revenues over the past 3 years. Each year, revenues have decreased by 9% per year.

The CEO of Swift Enterprises has hired your team to investigate why revenues have decreased and determine what can be done to increase revenues.

(Sample framework is on the following page)

<u>Sample Framework</u>: One potential framework could look like the following. The candidate does not need to have this exact framework, but should capture many of these points.

- Swift Revenues
    - Have prices decreased?
    - Has sales volume declined?
    - Has sales mix changed among products?

- Jet Ski Market
    - Has the market been declining?
    - Are there any new technologies or regulations impacting Swift's business?

- Swift's Competitors
    - Have competitors done something differently?
    - Are there any best practices we can take from competitors that are performing well?

- Jet Ski Consumers
    - Have needs or preferences changed?
    - Have purchasing behaviors changed?
    - Have consumers' perceptions of Swift changed?

<u>Question 1</u>: We have collected data on the jet ski market in the chart below. Based on this, what is your assessment of the market?

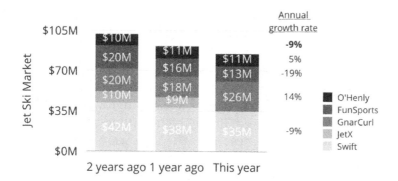

(Sample answer is on the following page)

<u>Answer to Question 1</u>: There are a few key takeaways from this chart.

The overall market has shrunk at 9% per year. Therefore, Swift is declining at the same rate as the market. In other words, they are an average performer

JetX has disappeared from the market. It is likely JetX was acquired by GarCurl because of the large increase in revenues during the period that JetX disappeared. It may be helpful to analyze JetX to see why they went out of business and why they were acquired

O'Henly has actually been able to grow at 5% per year despite an overall declining market. It may be helpful to analyze this player to see what their strategies or best practices are

<u>Question 2</u>: What are some revenue growth strategies?

(Sample answer is on the following page)

<u>Answer to Question 2</u>: We can think about revenue growth strategies as either inorganic growth, which is growth through acquisition, or organic growth, which is growth driven by the company internally. Organic growth can be further segmented into growth through existing revenue streams and growth through new revenue streams.

- Inorganic growth
  - o Make an acquisition of another Jet Ski player
  - o Merge with another Jet Ski player

- Organic growth: existing revenue streams
  - o Increase price
  - o Increase volume by going after new geographies, distribution channels, or customers
  - o Increase volume through marketing

- Organic revenue growth: new revenue streams
  - o Offer jet ski repair services
  - o Offer jet ski insurance or warranties
  - o Offer jet ski rentals
  - o Sell jet ski accessories, such as helmets or life jackets

<u>Question 3</u>: What was Swift's market share 2 years ago? What market share does Swift need to have next year in order to maintain the same revenues as 2 years ago? The market size next year is expected to be $80M.

(Sample answer is on the following page)

<u>Answer to Question 3</u>: We'll need to refer back to the previous chart in Question 1 in order to find Swift's market share 2 years ago.

Market size 2 years ago = $42M + $10M + $20M + $20M + $10M = $102M

Swift's revenue 2 years ago = $42M

Swift's market share 2 years ago = $42M / $102M = ~40% (rounded)

2 years ago, Swift had a market share of ~40%.

Market size next year = $80M

Market share next year required to maintain revenues from 2 years ago = $42M / $80M = ~50% (rounded)

To maintain the same revenues as 2 years ago, Swift needs a 50% market share, up from a 40% market share 2 years ago. This seems difficult to achieve given that the market is declining at -9% per year.

Question 4: Swift is considering running a special promotion to increase sales. Customers will receive a $1,500 gas card with each jet ski that they purchase. This would allow customers to redeem up to $1,500 worth of gas at Swift's expense. Swift expects 2 out of 3 customers to use this gas card. Customers that use this gas card will redeem an average of $1,200 of gas before the card expires.

Jet skis are sold for $7,000 and cost $2,000 to produce. Swift typically sells 5,000 jet skis in one year. This promotion is expected to increase the number of jet skis sold per year to 6,000. Assume the special promotion only applies to the incremental 1,000 jet skis sold.

How much will this promotion increase revenues and profits?

(Sample answer is on the following page)

Answer to Question 4: Let's calculate the increase in revenues first. Each jet ski sells for $7,000 and we expect the number of jet skis sold to increase from 5,000 to 6,000 with this promotion.

Therefore, revenues are expected to increase by $7,000 * 1,000 = $7M. This is a 20% increase in revenue compared to Swift's current annual revenue of $7,000 * 5,000 = $35M.

Next, let's calculate how much profits will increase.

Each jet ski sale gives customers a $1,500 gas card, which would cost Swift $1,500. However, only 2 out of 3 customers will use the gas card and among those customers, they would redeem an average of $1,200.

From this, the average cost of each gas card = $1,500 * (2/3) * ($1,200 / $1,500) = $800.

We know that jet skis cost $2,000 to produce.

Therefore, the increase in profits is 1,000 jet skis * ($7,000 - $2,000 - $800) = $4.2M.

This promotion will increase revenues by $7M and profits by $4.2M. Therefore, Swift should definitely run this promotion since it would increase their revenues by 20%.

<u>Conclusion</u>: The CEO of Swift Enterprises is eager to hear what you have to say. What is your recommendation?

(Sample conclusion is on the following page)

<u>Sample Conclusion</u>: One potential recommendation is presented below.

"Swift Enterprises' revenues have decreased at the same rate as the market, implying that the decline in the jet ski market is responsible for the decrease in revenues. In order to increase revenues, I recommend three things.

One, Swift should run a promotion in which they give customers that purchase a jet ski a $1,500 gas card. This promotion would increase revenues by $7M and profits by $4.2M.

Two, Swift should look into O'Henly's business strategies. This jet ski player has been growing at 5% despite a declining market. There could be meaningful opportunities to learn from their business strategies.

Three, Swift should consider acquiring another Jet Ski player. Another competitor has made a similar move and successfully absorbed the new revenues.

For next steps, I'd like to look into two areas. One, look into O'Henly more closely to understand what is driving their growth. Two, look into whether any of the other jet ski players would make an attractive acquisition target."

Practice Case #3 – Get-A-Ride

Difficulty: Medium

The Moscow airport has decided to issue 1,000 new taxi permits for $50,000 each per year. These permits allow taxi drivers to pick up passengers at the airport and drive them to their destinations.

Your client, Get-A-Ride, is a taxi company that has a fleet of cars and drivers. Currently, the taxi company only services customers in the city of Moscow and cannot pick up customers at the Moscow airport. Get-A-Ride has noticed that they have an excess capacity of cars and drivers available and is considering purchasing these new taxi permits.

Should your client purchase these new permits? If so, how many should they purchase?

(Sample framework is on the following page)

<u>Sample Framework</u>: One potential framework could look like the following. The candidate does not need to have this exact framework, but should capture many of these points.

- Airport taxi demand
    - o Is there any unmet passenger demand for taxis at airports?
    - o How many additional taxis are needed to meet demand?

- Get-A-Ride supply
    - o How much excess capacity of taxis does Get-A-Ride have?
    - o Would Get-A-Ride's drivers want to service airport passengers?

- Expected profitability
    - o What are the expected revenues?
    - o What are the expected costs?

- Competitor reaction
    - o Will competitors place a bid for the permits?
    - o How will competitors react to an increase in the supply of taxis at the airport?

<u>Question 1</u>: Are there enough taxis currently servicing airport customers?

- The airport handles 28.8M passengers every year

- You can assume there are 360 days per year

- 70% of passengers are from domestic flights and 30% are from international flights

- One-fourth of domestic passengers and two-thirds of international passengers use a taxi

- There are 1,000 taxis currently operating in the airport

- The average taxi trip takes one hour to pick up the passenger, drop them off at their destination, and return to the airport

- The average taxi fare is $150

- Assume there is one passenger per taxi trip

- 20% of demand occurs between 12AM and 8AM

- 60% of demand occurs between 8AM and 8PM

- 20% of demand occurs between 8PM and 12AM

- Cars require $10,000 per year for maintenance

- Profit margins for Get-A-Ride are typically 20% of the fare (rest of the fare goes towards paying for gas and driver costs)

(Sample answer is on the following page)

<u>Answer to Question 1</u>: We will first calculate daily demand for taxis and then compare that to the supply of taxis to see if the demand for taxis is fully being met.

28.8M passengers per year / 360 days per year = 80,000 passengers per day

Next, we'll calculate how many passengers use taxis.

80,000 passengers * 70% domestic * (1/4) domestic passengers use taxis = 14,000 domestic passengers that use taxis

80,000 passengers * 30% international * (2/3) international passengers use taxis = 16,000 international passengers that use taxis

Total passengers that use taxis = 14,000 + 16,000 = 30,000

We'll then determine the demand for taxis during each of the three different time periods we are given.

12AM-8AM: 30,000 passengers * 20% = 6,000 passengers need taxis
8AM-8PM: 30,000 passengers * 60% = 18,000 passengers need taxis
8PM-12AM: 30,000 passengers * 20% = 6,000 passengers need taxis

Afterward, we'll calculate the supply of taxis for each of the three different time periods.

12AM-8AM: 1,000 taxis * 8 hours * 1 trip per hour = 8,000 trips
8AM-8PM: 1,000 taxis * 12 hours * 1 trip per hour = 12,000 trips
8PM-12AM: 1,000 taxis * 4 hours * 1 trip her hour = 4,000 trips

There are not enough taxis servicing airport customers. From 8AM-8PM, 18,000 passengers need taxis, but existing taxis can only provide 12,000 trips. From 8PM-12AM, 6,000 passengers need taxis, but taxis can only provide 4,000 trips.

<u>Question 2</u>: How many additional taxis are needed?

(Sample answer is on the following page)

<u>Answer to Question 2</u>: Recall the following from Question 1:

Taxi demand:

- 12AM-8AM: 6,000 passengers need taxis

- 8AM-8PM: 18,000 passengers need taxis

- 8PM-12AM: 6,000 passengers need taxis

Taxi supply:

- 12AM-8AM: 8,000 trips supplied

- 8AM-8PM: 12,000 trips supplied

- 8PM-12AM: 4,000 trips supplied

Therefore, from 8AM-8PM, we are short by 6,000 trips and from 8PM-12AM, we are short by 2,000 trips.

We know that taxis can complete one trip per hour, so we can calculate the number of taxis needed.

8AM-8PM: 6,000 trips / 12 trips per taxi during this period = 500 additional taxis needed

8PM-12AM: 2,000 trips / 4 trips per taxi during this time period = 500 additional taxis needed

The Moscow airport needs an additional 500 taxis to meet demand. These taxis would need to drive from 8AM – 12AM each day.

<u>Question 3</u>: What is the expected annual increase in profit if Get-A-Ride purchases the taxi permits needed to service the unmet demand?

(Sample answer is on the following page)

<u>Answer to Question 3</u>: Get-A-Ride would service an additional 6,000 passengers between 8AM-8PM and an additional 2,000 passengers between 8PM-12AM.

Therefore, the total number of trips per day = 6,000 + 2,000 = 8,000 trips. We can now calculate annual revenues.

Revenue per day = 8,000 trips * $150 per trip * 20% profit margin = $240K per day

Revenue per year = $240K * 360 = $86.4M

Next, we'll calculate annual costs.

Annual permit costs = 500 taxis * $50K = $25M
Annual taxi maintenance costs = 500 * $10K = $5M
Total annual costs = $25M + $5M = $30M

We'll then subtract annual costs from annual revenues to determine the increase in annual profit.

Annual profit = $86.4M - $30M = $56.4M

Get-A-Ride should expect an annual increase in profits of $56.4M.

Question 4: What are some key assumptions we are making in our calculation of annual profits?

(Sample answer is on the following page)

<u>Answer to Question 4</u>: There are three key assumptions we are making.

One, we assumed that competitors would not purchase the remaining 500 permits and compete with Get-A-Ride. We could potentially buy all of the permits to block competitors from servicing the unmet airport passenger demand.

Two, we assumed that the price of $50,000 will not go up if multiple taxi companies bid a higher price to obtain these permits.

Three, we assumed that the airport will not offer more permits later, providing another opportunity for competitors to service the unmet airport passenger demand.

<u>Conclusion</u>: What is your recommendation?

(Sample conclusion is on the following page)

<u>Sample Conclusion</u>: For this problem, you could either recommend that Get-A-Ride should purchase 500 permits to meet unmet demand or Get-A-Ride should purchase the full 1,000 permits to ensure that competitors will not purchase the permits and compete with Get-A-Ride. One potential recommendation is presented below.

"I recommend that Get-A-Ride should acquire 1,000 taxi permits. There are three reasons that support this.

One, there is an unmet passenger demand for taxi transportation. Throughout the day, there are 8,000 potential trips that can be serviced if taxi permits are acquired.

Two, purchasing 1,000 taxi permits and servicing the unmet demand will increase profits by $31.4M per year.

Three, by purchasing all 1,000 permits, we can prevent competitors from entering and competing with us. Even though 500 permits will go unused, this is still highly profitable.

For next steps, I'd like to look into two areas. One, confirm with the airport that they will not be offering additional permits later on. Two, if competitors are also interested in obtaining the permit, determine how to acquire these permits before they do."

Practice Case #4 – GDS Systems

Difficulty: Easy

GDS Systems is a computer chip manufacturing company based in Dallas, Texas. They have been seeing declining profits over the past few years. As a result, they are looking to cut costs. They have identified one particular area where they could reduce costs: their corporate jet lease. GDS Systems currently leases a private jet in order to take their executives to and from meetings across the US.

GDS Systems' current private jet lease is expiring. Should they renew?

(Sample framework is on the following page)

<u>Sample Framework</u>: One potential framework could look like the following. The candidate does not need to have this exact framework, but should capture many of these points.

- GDS Systems' needs
    - o How many trips do executives take?
    - o How far do executives need to travel?
    - o What needs or preferences do executives have for travel?

- Jet Lease Terms
    - o How much does it cost to renew?
    - o How long is the lease term?
    - o How many executives or trips does the jet support?
    - o Does the jet currently meet the needs and preferences of executives?

- Current Jet Lease Alternatives
    - o Can the lease be negotiated down?
    - o Are there other private jet leases that are cheaper?
    - o Are commercial airlines an appropriate alternative?
    - o Can executive meetings be conducted online instead of in-person?

<u>Question 1</u>: Besides the cost of the jet lease, what are other costs that GDS Systems would likely need to account for if they renew the jet lease?

(Sample answer is on the following page)

Answer to Question 1: There are many other costs associated with using a private corporate jet besides the cost of the jet lease. We can think about these costs as either variable costs or fixed costs. Variable costs vary depending on the number of trips taken. Fixed costs must be paid regardless of how many trips are taken.

- Variable costs
  - Fuel
  - Cleaning and maintenance
  - Food and beverage service
  - Crew

- Fixed costs
  - Insurance
  - Airport landing license fees

Question 2: Based on the following information, how much would it cost if executives were to use commercial flights instead of a private jet?

On average, there are 5 executives that go on each trip. Assume that executives return to Dallas at the end of each trip.

Destination	# of trips per year	One-way distance	Price per ticket
Houston	80	300 miles	$200
Chicago	60	1,000 miles	$300
New York	150	1,500 miles	$350

(Sample answer is on the following page)

<u>Answer to Question 2</u>: We can calculate the total commercial flight costs per year by using the following formula for each city destination. Note that we need to multiply by 2 to get the round-trip costs since executives return to Dallas at the end of each trip.

Total flight cost = Number of trips per year * Average number of executives per trip * 2 * Price per ticket

Annual costs to fly to Houston = 80 * 5 * 2 * $200 = $160,000

Annual costs to fly to Chicago = 60 * 5 * 2 * $300 = $180,000

Annual costs to fly to New York = 150 * 5 * 2 * $350 = $525,000

Total annual flight costs = $160,000 + $180,000 + $525,500 = $865,000

It would cost $865,000 per year to use commercial flights to transport executives. We should compare this to the cost of the current private jet lease.

Question 3: GDS Systems' jet lease costs $800K per year. However, the costs of fuel, crew, insurance, and airport fees typically increase actual annual costs by 25%.

GDS Systems has looked into a couple of other jet lease options. Based on the following table, what conclusions can you draw?

	Alternative Option 1	Alternative Option 2	Alternative Option 3
Maximum one-way distance	1,300	1,600	1,800
Maximum # of passengers	9	4	12
Annual cost of lease	$600K	$500K	$700K

(Sample answer is on the following page)

<u>Answer to Question 3</u>: We first need to systematically look at each of the alternative jet lease options to determine if they meet the needs of GDS Systems.

The distance from Dallas to New York is 1,500 miles, so Alternative Option 1 will not be able to make this trip. Since executives take 150 trips to New York each year, this is not a viable option.

The average number of executives per trip is 5. Alternative Option 2 can only take a maximum of 4 passengers. Therefore, this option is also not viable because the jet would not be able to accommodate enough passengers for most trips.

This leaves us with Alternative Option 3, which is both capable of flying the distance to New York and can carry a sufficient number of executives each trip. The cost of this option is $700K, which is cheaper than the current jet lease. However, we need to account for the costs of crew, insurance, and airport fees in order to compare it to the cost of using commercial airplanes.

The total cost of the current jet lease is $800K * 1.25 = $1M.

The total cost of Alternative Option 3 is $700K * 1.25 = $875K.

Therefore, the total costs for Alternative Option 3 are $875K, which is cheaper than the current jet lease, which has a total cost of $1M. However, Alternative Option 3 is more expensive than using commercial airlines by $10K.

<u>Question 4</u>: What are the potential risks of using commercial airlines instead of a private jet?

(Sample answer is on the following page)

<u>Answer to Question 4</u>: We can think about risks as logistical risks and non-logistical risks.

- Logistical risks
  - o A limited selection of flight departure and arrival times
  - o Possibility of no capacity on flights
  - o Executives may miss their flights
  - o Flights may have layovers, which increases the likelihood of delays and flight cancellations

- Non-logistical risks
  - o Executives may be unhappy because flying commercial is less comfortable
  - o Executives may be more likely to get sick since commercial planes carry a larger number of passengers

<u>Conclusion</u>: Based on your findings, what is your recommendation?

(Sample conclusion is on the following page)

<u>Sample Conclusion</u>: For this problem, you could either recommend that GDS Systems use commercial airlines or recommend the Alternative Option 3 jet lease. These options cost $865K and $875K respectively, both of which are cheaper than the current $1M jet lease. One potential recommendation is presented below.

"I recommend that GDS Systems does not renew their current jet lease and instead sign a jet lease with Alternative Option 3. There are two reasons that support this.

One, signing a jet lease with Alternative Option 3 would cost $875K per year. This is 12.5% cheaper than the current jet lease option, which would cost $1M per year.

Two, although flying commercial would save an additional $10K, the incremental cost savings would not justify the risks that GDS Systems would take on by flying commercial. Logistical risks include the possibility of executives missing their flights or being unable to find a flight that fits their schedule. Non-logistical risks include executives being unhappy or getting sick on commercial flights.

For next steps, I'd like to look into whether the jet lease of Alternative Option 3 can be further negotiated down by signing a multi-year agreement."

Practice Case #5 - Chariott

Difficulty: Medium

Chariott is a US luxury hotel chain that provides room accommodations for personal and business travelers. Over the past few years, they have been seeing a decline in profits. They have hired us to help them determine what is causing the decline in profits and what they can do about this.

(Sample framework is on the following page)

<u>Sample Framework</u>: One potential framework could look like the following. The candidate does not need to have this exact framework, but should capture many of these points.

- Profitability drivers
    - o Have revenues declined?
        - Have the prices for rooms changed?
        - Have the number of rooms booked declined?
        - Has the mix of rooms booked changed?
    - o Have costs increased?
        - Have fixed costs increased?
        - Have variable costs increased?

- Hotel market
    - o Is the hotel market declining?
    - o Are there new technologies impacting the market?
    - o Are there new regulations impacting the market?

- Chariott Competitors
    - o Are competitors also experiencing a decline in profitability?
    - o Have competitors made any recent major moves?

- Hotel customers
    - o Have customer needs or preferences changed?
    - o Have customer purchasing behaviors changed?
    - o Have customer perceptions of Chariott changed?

Question 1: Based on the following chart of Chariott's costs, what conclusions can you draw?

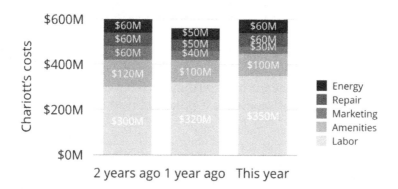

(Sample answer is on the following page)

<u>Answer to Question 1</u>: Although labor costs have increased and amenities and marketing costs have decreased, costs overall have remained flat over the past few years. Therefore, Chariott's decline in profits must be driven by a decline in revenues.

While it may be interesting to investigate why labor costs have gone up and why Chariott has decreased their marketing and amenities spend, this is not relevant to determining what is causing Chariott's decline in profits. This could be a potential next step once you have solved the case.

Question 2: Chariott offers three different types of rooms: economy, standard, and luxury. Based on the following table, what conclusions can you draw?

	Price per night	# of nights booked 2 years ago	# of nights booked this year
Economy rooms	$250	500K	600K
Standard rooms	$400	1.25M	1M
Luxury rooms	$600	200K	200K

(Sample answer is on the following page)

Answer to Question 2: Prices for the different rooms have remained the same over the past three years. Since costs have been flat and prices have remained the same, the decline in profitability must be driven by a decline in the volume of rooms booked.

In this table, we see that the number of nights booked for standard rooms has dropped by 20%. The number of nights booked for luxury rooms has been flat and the number of nights booked for economy rooms has actually increased by 20%.

However, because standard rooms are pricier than economy rooms and because there are more standard rooms than economy rooms, overall revenues have decreased.

Therefore, Chariott's decline in profitability is driven by the decline in the number of nights booked in standard rooms.

<u>Question 3</u>: By what percentage have revenues declined? What is the new profit margin?

(Sample answer is on the following page)

<u>Answer to Question 3</u>: We'll first calculate what revenues were 2 years ago and what revenues were this year.

Revenue 2 years ago = (500K * $250) + (1.25M * $400) + (200K * $600) = 745M

Revenue today = (600K * $250) + (1M * $400) + (200K * $600) = 670M

Percentage change in revenue = (670M - 745M) / 745M = -75M / 745M = -10% (rounded)

Revenues have decreased by 75M, or by roughly 10%. This is driven by a decline in the number of nights booked in standard rooms. This decline would be even greater if the number of economy nights booked had not grown over this time period.

For the second question, we know that total costs 2 years ago were $600M and they were also $600M this year. These numbers are taken from the chart in Question 1.

We can now calculate what the new profit margin is.

Profit margin this year = ($670M - 600M) / $670M = $70M / $670M = 10% (rounded)

Profit margin 2 years ago = ($745M - $600M) / $745M = $145M / $745M = 19% (rounded)

The new profit margin is 10%. This is down from Chariott's profit margin 2 years ago, which was 19%.

Question 4: You find out that a major competitor has recently launched a customer loyalty program that rewards customers for staying in standard rooms. For every four nights that a customer stays in a standard room, they will receive a fifth night free that they can use whenever they want within a year.

Chariott currently has no customer loyalty program and is considering creating a similar program. They want to create a program that is even better than that of competitors. Therefore, a key difference is that Chariott's customer loyalty program would apply to any type of room that is booked. For example, if a customer books four nights in an economy room, they could get one night in a luxury room for free, pending availability.

Because their hotel rooms are usually not utilized 100% of the time and because not all customers will redeem their free nights before they expire, the annual cost of such a program would be about $80M. Chariott believes that they can increase the annual number of nights booked in economy, standard, and luxury by the following amounts.

- Economy: 200K nights booked increase per year

- Standard: 200K nights booked increase per year

- Luxury: 50K nights booked increase per year

Will launching this program increase profits?

(Sample answer is on the following page)

<u>Answer to Question 4</u>: We will first calculate the increase in revenues from this program.

Increase in revenues = (200K * $250) + (200K * $400) + (50K * $600) = $160M.

The cost of the program is $80M. Therefore, the increase in profits is $160M - $80M = $80M.

By launching this program, profits will increase by $80M. Therefore, Chariott's profits will increase from $670M to $750, which is roughly equal to what Chariott's profits were two years ago. This program would effectively reverse Chariott's decline in profits.

<u>Conclusion</u>: You bump into the CEO of Chariott in the elevator on your way back from lunch. He asks you for a quick update on the work that you have done. What do you say?

(Sample conclusion is on the following page)

Sample Conclusion: One potential recommendation is presented below.

"Chariott's decline in profits is due to a decline in the number of nights booked for standard rooms. This is driven by competitors launching a customer loyalty program. To address this, I recommend that Chariott launch their own customer loyalty program for the following three reasons.

One, there is evidence that customer loyalty programs work. As a result of competitors' customer loyalty programs, Chariott has seen their number of nights booked in standard rooms decline from 1.25M nights to 1M nights. Competitors likely took these bookings.

Two, Chariott's hotel rooms are not utilized 100% of the time and not all customers will redeem their free nights before they expire. Therefore, these factors would help reduce the costs of this customer loyalty program.

Three, the program is expected to increase Chariott's profits by $80M. This would bring Chariott's profit levels back to what they were two years ago.

For next steps, I'd like to look into two areas. One, I'd like to look into the potential risks of launching this program. How will competitors respond? Is the uplift in nights booked and revenue sustainable? Two, I'd like to look into why labor costs have increased. There could be an opportunity to further increase profits by decreasing labor costs."

THE ULTIMATE CASE INTERVIEW WORKBOOK

Practice Case #6 – PharmaX

Difficulty: Hard

Our client is PharmaX, a large pharmaceutical company headquartered in Switzerland that has $20B a year in revenue. They have several blockbuster drugs, including drugs that treat arthritis, high blood pressure, and diabetes.

PharmaX is interested in entering a rapidly growing segment of the market called biosimilars, which are manufactured products with high molecular complexity that are almost an identical copy of an original product that is manufactured by another company. Biosimilars represent an opportunity for PharmaX to increase revenues by selling copycat drugs of competitor drugs once competitors' patents expire.

The process to manufacture biosimilars is very complicated and requires a specialized facility and specialized manufacturing knowledge.

Because of this, PharmaX is considering making an acquisition of Biologics, a top biosimilars start-up based in San Diego, California.

Should PharmaX acquire Biologics?

(Sample framework is on the following page)

<u>Sample Framework</u>: One potential framework could look like the following. The candidate does not need to have this exact framework, but should capture many of these points.

- Biosimilars market attractiveness
  - What is the market size?
  - What is the market growth rate?
  - What are the average profit margins?

- Biologics attractiveness
  - What are the company's revenues and profits?
  - What does the company's drug pipeline look like?
  - How strong is their biosimilars manufacturing process?
  - How strong is their expertise in biosimilars?

- Financial implications
  - Is the acquisition price fair?
  - What is the expected return on investment from this acquisition?

- Strategic alternatives
  - Can PharmaX develop biosimilars capabilities internally?
  - Would a partnership or joint venture make more sense?
  - Are there other potential acquisition targets?

Question 1: The corporate development team at PharmaX wants to first assess Biologics' current drug portfolio. What considerations would you look into?

(Sample answer is on the following page)

<u>Answer to Question 1</u>: We can think about considerations as either short-term considerations and long-term considerations.

- Short-term considerations
    - What are the revenues and profits of drugs that are currently being sold?
    - What is the number of competitor drugs that are in these segments?
    - What customer segments are these drugs targeted to and are these segments attractive?
    - What are the risks of these drugs in terms of potential lawsuits?

- Long-term considerations
    - How much longer do currently approved drugs have on their patents?
    - How much will it cost to sustain research for drugs in development?
    - How likely are these drugs to pass clinical trials and get approval to sell to consumers?
    - Are competitors developing any competing drugs or substitutes to drugs in PharmaX's pipeline?

Question 2: In order for a drug to receive Food and Drug Administration (FDA) approval, a drug needs to pass four different stages in the following order: Phase I clinical trials, Phase II clinical trials, Phase III clinical trials, and Filing.

Biologics has one potential blockbuster drug that is in development and is just about to start Phase I clinical trials. Looking further ahead, if PharmaX were to acquire Biologics, PharmaX was thinking of investing an additional $200M in Biologics' upcoming Phase II clinical trials in order to improve the likelihood that Biologics' drug will pass Phase II.

How much would the Phase II success rate need to increase in order to justify the investment? If the drug is successfully developed and passes all four stages needed to get FDA approval, the present value of future profits for the drug would be $2B.

Additional information to consider:

- 75% of drugs pass Phase I clinical trials

- The ratio of failed drugs to successful drugs in Phase II clinical trials is 2:1

- 1 in 2 drugs pass Phase III clinical trials

- Historically, 240/300 drugs have passed the Filing stage

(Sample answer is on the following page)

<u>Answer to Question 2</u>: We need to first work backward to determine how much the drug is worth if it passes Phase II clinical trials. We know that the chance of passing Phase III is 50% (1/2) and the chance of passing filing is 80% (240/300). Therefore, there is a 50% * 80% = 40% chance of the drug making it to market following completion of Phase II clinical trials.

The drug is worth $2B if it makes it to market, so we know that the drug is worth $2B * 40% = $800M right after it has passed Phase II.

In order to break even, the value of the drug after Phase II would need to be $800M + $200M = $1B since PharmaX is investing an additional $200M in the drug's research and development. This represents an increase of $200M / $800M = 25% on the value of the drug after completing Phase II. Therefore, the probability that the drug passes Phase I and Phase II needs to increase by 25% as well in order to break even on the investment.

The probability that the drug passes Phase I is 75% and the probability that it passes Phase II is 33.33% (1/3). Therefore, the probability that the drug passes Phase I and Phase II is 75% * (33.33%) = 25%.

In order for the probability that the drug passes Phase I and Phase II to be 50% (25% base case + 25% increase needed to break even), Phase II probability needs to increase to 66.66%, doubling.

As a check, we see that the new probability of passing Phase I and Phase II clinical trials is 75% * 66.66% = 50%.

Phase II success rate would need to be 66.66% in order to break even on this investment. This seems challenging since the success rate would need to double.

Question 3: The second potential blockbuster drug for Biologics has passed all four stages needed for FDA approval. The patent for this drug expires after 15 years. Biologics expects to sell 20M pills each year for the first 10 years and 10M pills each year for the following 5 years afterward. Biologics believes that after the patent expires, they will receive very little sales and revenue as competitors can sell generic versions of their drug. Each pill sells for $3 and costs pennies to make.

A competitor is making a similar drug and there is a two-thirds likelihood that they will receive FDA approval. If the competitor drug receives FDA approval, they would launch their drug roughly at the same time as Biologics and their drug would also have 15 years remaining on their patent. Assume that if the competitor launches their drug, they would take 40% of Biologics' sales volume.

To increase drug sales, PharmaX is considering investing $120M in marketing over the life of the drug's patent. If the competitor's drug does not launch, then marketing is expected to increase sales by 20%. If the competitor's drug does launch, marketing is expected to increase sales by 10%.

What is the expected return on investment for this marketing campaign?

(Sample answer is on the following page)

Answer to Question 3: There are two scenarios we need to consider: the scenario in which the competitor does not launch their drug and the scenario in which they do launch their drug. We'll then calculate the incremental profit the marketing investment would generate under both scenarios in order to calculate the expected value of the increase in profit.

If the competitor does not launch their drug, Biologics expects to sell (20M * 10) + (10M * 5) = 250M pills. The marketing investment will increase sales by 20%, or by 250M * 20% = 50M pills.

Each pill sells for $3 and we can assume that the cost to produce each pill is basically zero since the problem indicated that each pill costs pennies to make. Therefore, Biologics will gain an additional 50M * $3 = $150M in profit under this scenario.

If the competitor does launch their drug, Biologics expects to sell 250M pills * (1 – 40%) = 150M pills since the competitor would take 40% of Biologics' sales volume. In this scenario, the marketing investment will increase sales by 10% or by 150M * 10% = 15M.

Therefore, Biologics will gain an additional 15M * $3 = $45M in profit under this scenario.

The expected value of the increase in profit from this marketing campaign is the sum of the likelihood of each scenario times their respective increase in profits.

Expected value of marketing campaign = (1/3 * $150M) + (2/3 * $45M) = $80M.

We can now calculate the return on investment of this marketing campaign that costs $120M.

Return on investment = ($80M - $120M) / $120M = -33.33%

The marketing campaign will generate $80M in additional profit, but at a cost of $120M. Therefore, PharmaX should not make this investment since it has a -33% return on investment.

<u>Question 4</u>: Following the acquisition, PharmaX would want to fully integrate Biologics into their company. What are some challenges of such an integration?

(Sample answer is on the following page)

<u>Answer to Question 4</u>: We can think about integration challenges as logistical challenges and non-logistical challenges.

- Logistical challenges
    o Language barriers
    o Time zone differences
    o Corporate buildings are far from each other

- Non-logistical challenges
    o Company culture differences
    o Different knowledge and expertise among employees
    o People may leave Biologics following the acquisition

<u>Conclusion</u>: There is no summary or recommendation needed for this case.

Practice Case #7 – AG&E

Difficulty: Easy

Our client, AG&E, is a utility company that is the sole provider of utilities in Delaware. AG&E is regulated by the government and cannot earn more than 15% of their assets as income. They have a capacity of 2M megawatt hours (MWh) per year, which all comes from nonrenewable energy sources, such as coal and petroleum.

Recently, the government has created a mandate that for every megawatt hour that is produced from nonrenewable energy sources, 0.05 megawatt hours need to be produced from renewable energy sources. AG&E has two different options to meet this mandate.

Option A: AG&E can purchase clean energy credits from a third party, which would count as producing energy from a renewable energy source.

Option B: AG&E can invest in building a wind farm, consisting of many wind turbines, to generate renewable energy to meet this mandate.

What should AG&E do?

(Sample framework is on the following page)

Sample Framework: One potential framework could look like the following. The candidate does not need to have this exact framework, but should capture many of these points.

- Costs
    - What are all of the costs involved in building a wind farm?
    - How much do clean energy credits cost?
    - Which option is most cost-effective?

- Benefits
    - Will customers or the government view AG&E more favorably if they build a wind farm?
    - Would building a wind farm allow AG&E to earn more income since their assets have increased?

- AG&E wind farm capabilities
    - Does AG&E have the capital required to build a wind farm?
    - Does AG&E know how to build and operate a wind farm?

- Risks
    - What are the risks of building a wind farm?
    - What are the risks of purchasing clean energy credits?
    - Can these risks be managed?

Question 1: Based on the following information, is it cheaper for AG&E to purchase clean energy credits or to build a wind farm?

Clean energy credits:

- Today, credits cost $40 per MWh

- Three years ago, credits cost $10 per MWh

Wind farm:

- To set up enough turbines with an annual capacity of 1 MWh would cost $4,000

- Wind farms typically last for 40 years

- Assume there are no annual maintenance costs

(Sample answer is on the following page)

<u>Answer to Question 1</u>: Let's first calculate how many MWh of renewable energy AG&E is required to produce. Recall that AG&E has a capacity of 2M MWh.

2M MWh * 0.05 = 100K MWh of renewable energy needed

Cost to purchase clean energy credits = 100K MWh * $40 per MWh = $4M

Cost to build wind farm = ($4,000 per MWh * 100K MWh) / 40 = $10M

It is cheaper for AG&E to purchase clean energy credits. This would cost $4M per year compared to $10M per year if they decided to build a wind farm.

Question 2: Assume that AG&E's customers would absorb all of the costs if AG&E were to either purchase the clean energy credits or build a wind farm. If AG&E purchases clean energy credits, the utility rate charged to customers would increase from $0.25 to $0.26 per kilowatt hour. What would the new utility rate be if AG&E built a wind farm?

(Sample answer is on the following page)

Answer to Question 2: First, we'll calculate the percentage increase in the utility rate if AG&E purchases clean energy credits.

A rate increase from $0.25 to $0.26 is a 4% increase.

We know that purchasing clean energy credits would cost $4M. So, utility rate increases by 4% if costs increase by $4M. Building a wind farm costs $10M, so we'd expect the utility rate to increase even more.

$10M is 2.5 times as large as $4M. From this, we calculate that the utility rate increase if AG&E builds a wind farm is 2.5 * 4% = 10% increase.

Therefore, the utility rate would be $0.25 * 1.1 = $0.275.

You could have also performed this calculation in one step: utility rate increase = ($10M / $4M) * 4% * $0.25 + $0.25 = $0.275.

If AG&E builds a wind farm, the utility rate would increase from $0.25 to $0.275, a 10% increase.

Question 3: What are the advantages and disadvantages of purchasing clean energy credits versus building a wind farm?

(Sample answer is on the following page)

<u>Answer to Question 3</u>: We can structure our answer by listing the advantages and disadvantages of each option.

Clean energy credits:

- \+ Cheaper option

- \+ Quicker to implement

- \+ Easier to change plans if regulations change

- – Clean energy credit prices have been increasing drastically over the past few years and could continue to increase

- – Not a long-term solution for producing clean energy

Wind farm:

- \+ Potentially improves AG&E's brand image in the eyes of customers and the government

- \+ Increases maximum allowable income for the company since assets increase

- – Large upfront capital investment required

- – Takes longer to implement

- – Requires having wind farm expertise

- – More difficult to change plans if regulations change

<u>Conclusion</u>: Which option should AG&E pursue?

(Sample conclusion is on the following page)

<u>Sample Conclusion</u>: You can recommend either option for this case as long as you have compelling reasons to justify your position. One potential recommendation is presented below.

"I recommend that AG&E builds a wind farm to meet the government's renewable energy production mandate. There are three reasons to support this.

One, by building a wind farm, AG&E increases their maximum allowable income. The government mandates that AG&E cannot earn more than 15% of their assets as income. Therefore, by increasing their assets, AG&E can increase their maximum allowable income.

Two, although purchasing clean energy credits is a cheaper option than building a wind farm, clean energy credit prices have been increasing drastically. Over the past three years, clean energy prices have quadrupled. If this trend continues, purchasing clean energy credits may become a more expensive option than building a wind farm.

Three, building a wind farm would improve AG&E's brand image in the eyes of customers and the government. This could provide benefits, such as an increase in the number of customers or relaxed scrutiny from the government.

For next steps, I'd like to look into two areas. One, confirm that AG&E has the capital and expertise to build and operate a wind farm. Two, assess the risks of building a wind farm."

Practice Case #8 – Hens Co.

Difficulty: Medium

Your client is a private equity firm that is considering acquiring Hens Co., which owns a large chicken farm that produces eggs. The business model for Hens Co. is simple. They own hens on their farm, which lay eggs that are sold to egg vendors.

The businesses that the private equity firm already owns all have nothing to do with eggs, so there are practically no synergies. However, the private equity firm is looking to diversify their portfolio of businesses. They are interested in acquiring Hens Co. if they are an attractive, high-performing business.

Should your client acquire Hens Co.?

(Sample framework is on the following page)

<u>Sample Framework</u>: One potential framework could look like the following. The candidate does not need to have this exact framework, but should capture many of these points.

- Egg market attractiveness
    - What is the market size?
    - What is the market growth rate?
    - What are average profit margins in the market?

- Hens Co. attractiveness
    - Is Hens Co. profitable?
    - What is the competitive positioning of Hens Co.?
    - Does Hens Co. have any competitive advantages or differentiation?

- Private equity firm capabilities
    - Does the private equity firm know how to run and manage an egg farm?
    - Will the private equity firm be able to grow the business or improve profit margins?

- Acquisition price
    - What is the acquisition price?
    - How long will it take to break even on this acquisition?

Question 1: What is Hens Co.'s market share? Your client only wants to acquire Hens Co. if they have at least a 51% market share.

Assume that there are only three players in the egg market. Regular eggs sell for $1.20 per dozen while jumbo eggs sell for $2.40 per dozen.

Number of hens:

- Hens Co. has 200,000 hens

- Egg Corp has 150,000 hens

- Yolk LLC has 100,000 hens

Hen productivity:

- Hens Co.'s hens each lay 6 eggs per week

- Egg Corp's hens each lay 4 eggs per week

- Yolk LLC's hens each lay 3 eggs per week

Jumbo eggs:

- Hens Co.'s eggs have a 1 in 3 chance of being jumbo

- Egg Corp's eggs have a 1 in 5 chance of being jumbo

- Yolk LLC's eggs have a 1 in 6 chance of being jumbo

(Sample answer is on the following page)

Answer to Question 1: To calculate Hens Co.'s market share, we will calculate Hens Co.'s revenues in one week and divide by the total market's revenues in one week.

First, we'll calculate how many eggs each player produces per week.

Hens Co: 200K hens * 6 eggs per hen = 1.2M eggs per week
Egg Corp: 150K hens * 4 eggs per hen = 600K eggs per week
Yolk LLC: 100K hens * 3 eggs per hen = 300K eggs per week

Next, we'll need to calculate how many of the eggs produced are regular eggs versus jumbo eggs since these eggs command different prices.

Hens Co: 1.2M eggs * (1/3) = 400K jumbo eggs, 800K regular eggs
Egg Corp: 600K * (1/5) = 120K jumbo eggs, 480K regular eggs
Yolk LLC: 300K * (1/6) = 50K jumbo eggs, 250K regular eggs

We'll then calculate how much regular eggs and jumbo eggs sell for.

Regular eggs = $1.20 per dozen / 12 eggs = $0.10 per egg
Jumbo eggs = $2.40 per dozen / 12 eggs = $0.20 per egg

With this, we can calculate the revenues for each player per week.

Hens Co. revenues: (400K * $0.20) + (800K * $0.10) = $160K
Egg Corp revenues: (120K * $0.20) + (480K * $0.10) = $72K
Yolk LLC revenues: (50K * $0.20) + (250K * $0.10) = $35K

Finally, we can calculate Hens Co.'s market share.

Hens Co.'s market share = $160K / ($160K + $72K + $35K) = 60% (rounded)

Hens Co. has a 60% market share. Therefore, Hens Co. is an attractive acquisition target since they meet the client's requirement of having at least a 51% market share.

<u>Question 2</u>: What are the potential costs of running an egg farm?

(Sample answer is on the following page)

<u>Answer to Question 2</u>: We can think about costs as fixed costs and variable costs.

- Fixed costs
  - Land
  - Farm equipment or machinery
  - Trucks for transportation
  - Farm insurance

- Variable costs
  - Chickens
  - Chicken feed
  - Labor

Question 3: Your client will only acquire Hens Co. if they have at least double the profit margin of any competitor.

Assume that the only costs in this line of business are chicken feed and land. Chicken feed costs $0.60 per dozen eggs produced for all players. Hens Co.'s land costs are $40K per week. In general, land costs scale with the number of hens on the farm.

Based on this, what is Hens Co.'s profit margin compared to competitors?

(Sample answer is on the following page)

<u>Answer to Question 3</u>: Recall that we have already calculated the number of eggs produced by each player and the revenues per week for each player.

Hens Co: 1.2M eggs per week
Egg Corp: 600K eggs per week
Yolk LLC: 300K eggs per week

Hens Co. revenues: $160K per week
Egg Corp revenues: $72K per week
Yolk LLC revenues: $35K per week

We know that chicken feed costs $0.60 per dozen eggs or $0.05 per egg. So, we'll calculate chicken feed costs for each player.

Hens Co. chicken feed costs: 1.2M eggs * $0.05 = $60K per week
Egg Corp chicken feed costs: 600K * $0.05 = $30K per week
Yolk LLC chicken feed costs: 300K * $0.05 = $15K per week

Next, we'll calculate land costs for each player, which scales with the number of hens on the farm.

Hens Co. land: $40K per week
Egg Corp land: $40K * (150K hens / 200K hens) = $30K per week
Yolk LLC land: $40K * (100K hens / 200K hens) = $20K per week

Finally, we can calculate the profit margin.

Hens Co. profit margin: ($160K - $60K - $40K) / $160K = 37.5%
Egg Corp profit margin: ($72K - $30K - $30K) / $72K = 16.7%
Yolk LLC profit margin: ($35K - $15K - $20K) / $35K = 0%

Hens Co. has a profit margin of 37.5%, which is more than double that of any competitor. Therefore, Hens Co. is an attractive acquisition target.

<u>Question 4</u>: What are the potential risks of entering the egg market?

(Sample answer is on the following page)

<u>Answer to Question 4</u>: We can think about risks as internal risks, which are risks specific to our private equity client, and external risks, which are risks related to the market, competitors, or customers.

- Internal risks
  - o Our client may not be able to keep Hens Co.'s hens alive
  - o Our client may not be able to maintain Hens Co.'s productivity in egg production

- External risks
  - o The price of eggs could change
  - o The cost of chicken feed could change
  - o Customers could switch to purchasing eggs from competitors
  - o Consumers could switch to egg substitutes or alternatives
  - o Competitors may try to steal Hens Co.'s customers

<u>Conclusion</u>: Based on your analysis and findings, should your client acquire Hens Co.?

(Sample conclusion is on the following page)

<u>Sample Conclusion</u>: One potential recommendation is presented below.

"I recommend that our client acquires Hens Co. There are three reasons to support this.

One, Hens Co. is the market leader with a 60% market share. This satisfies our client's requirement that Hens Co. has at least a 51% market share.

Two, Hens Co. has a profit margin of 37.5%, which is significantly higher than that of competitors. This satisfies our client's requirement that Hens Co. has a profit margin that is double that of any competitor.

Three, Hens Co. has competitive advantages over the other players. Their hens produce more eggs per week and have a higher likelihood of producing jumbo eggs.

For next steps, I'd like to look into two areas. One, look into whether our client has the experience and capabilities to run an egg farm. Two, look into the acquisition price to determine if it is fair and reasonable."

Practice Case #9 – Surfside

Difficulty: Hard

Surfside is a family owned business that produces surfboards in the US. A large national retail chain that sells gear and equipment for extreme sports has recently contacted Surfside about signing a contract to buy 25,000 surfboards from Surfside every year for the next 5 years. Unfortunately, Surfside's existing factory can only handle producing 5,000 surfboards per year.

Surfside has hired us to help them determine how to best scale their production to meet the increased demand.

(No framework necessary. Proceed straight to the first question)

Question 1: Surfside is considering building a new factory to increase production. Based on the following information, how should they set up the new factory and how much would it cost?

Due to space constraints, the factory can only support having three machines. There are three types of production machines available:

- Machine type A: produces 5,000 surfboards per year and costs $400K

- Machine type B: produces 7,000 surfboards per year and costs $700K

- Machine type C: produces 10,000 surfboards per year and costs $1.1M

(Sample answer is on the following page)

<u>Answer to Question 1</u>: Currently, Surfside can only produce 5,000 surfboards per year and they need to produce at least 25,000 surfboards per year. Therefore, they need to increase production capacity by at least 20,000 surfboards per year.

From initial inspection, we see that machine type A costs $80 per surfboard produced, machine type B costs $100 per surfboard produced, and machine type C costs $110 per surfboard produced. Therefore, machine type A is the cheapest while machine type C is the most expensive.

There are a few combinations of machines that can produce 20,000 surfboards:

- 2 machine type C

- 1 machine type C + 2 machine type A

- 3 machine type B

We can also logically rule out the following combinations:

- 1 machine type C + 2 machine type B: ruled out because machine type A is cheaper than B

- 1 machine type C + 1 machine type B + 1 machine type A: ruled out because machine type A is cheaper than B

- 3 machine type A: ruled out because this does not produce at least 20,000 surfboards

2 machine type C = 20,000 capacity
Cost = 2 * $1.1M = $2.2M

1 machine type C + 2 machine type A = 20,000 capacity
Cost = $1.1M + (2 * $400K) = $1.9M

3 machine type B = 21,000 capacity
Cost = 3 * $700K = $2.1M

The most cost-effective configuration is having 1 machine type C and 2 machine type A. This will produce 20,000 surfboards per year at a cost of $1.9M. We should compare this cost to other options, such as expanding the current factory.

Question 2: Another option Surfside is considering is expanding their current factory, which would also cost $1.9M. Costs aside, what are other considerations you would want to consider in order to decide whether Surfside should expand their current factory or set up a new factory?

(Sample answer is on the following page)

<u>Answer to Question 2</u>: We can think about considerations as cost considerations and production considerations.

- Cost considerations
    - o Having one factory would lower management and administrative costs
    - o Having two factories could lower distribution costs if the factories are in different locations

- Production considerations
    - o It is easier to standardize production if there is only one factory
    - o Having two factories helps diversify risk
    - o Building a new factory could take a longer time than expanding the current one, resulting in lost production time

<u>Question 3</u>: Do you think Surfside should build a new factory or expand their existing factory?

(Sample answer is on the following page)

<u>Answer to Question 3</u>: You can recommend either option for this question as long as you provide logical, compelling reasons. One potential answer could look like the following:

"I believe that Surfside should expand their existing factory. There are three reasons to support this.

One, by expanding their existing factory, Surfside could lower management and administrative costs since they are only dealing with one factory.

Two, by having a single factory, Surfside can better manage and standardize production to ensure consistent quality across all surfboards that are produced.

Three, setting up a new factory would likely take longer to implement than expanding the existing factory. This would lead to lost production time."

<u>Question 4</u>: If you were the CEO of Surfside, what would be the one or two big issues regarding this expansion project that would keep you up at night?

(Sample answer is on the following page)

Answer to Question 4: There is no structure needed for this answer since it is only asking for one or two ideas. A variety of different answers could be given, including the following:

- Not being able to meet increased demand from the national retail chain

- Not being able to meet increased demand from other potential retailers

- Experiencing a decrease in production quality from rushing to scale production

- Losing negotiation power by entering into a contract with such a large retailer

- Having a loss of focus on innovating newer and better surfboards

Question 5: One of the big issues on the CEO's mind is being able to execute on increasing production.

Due to operational risks, such as labor shortages, power outages, and delays in the delivery of raw materials, Surfside believes there is a 20% chance they will only be able to produce 20,000 surfboards. If they fall short of producing 25,000 surfboards, then they will lose all of the profits from the surfboards they were unable to produce.

Surfside is considering purchasing insurance that would pay them for the lost profits in this scenario. The insurance company typically sets up their insurance pricing such that the insurance company has a 10% profit margin.

How much would you expect this insurance to cost?

Additional information:

- Surfboards sell for $200 each

- Assume it costs $1.9M to produce 25,000 surfboards

(Sample answer is on the following page)

<u>Answer to Question 5</u>: We need to calculate the expected value of lost profits based on the assumption that there is a 20% chance Surfside will only be able to produce 20,000 surfboards. To do this, we first need to determine Surfside's profit per surfboard.

Recall from the previous problem that it costs $1.9M to produce 25,000 surfboards. Therefore, a single surfboard costs $1.9M / 25,000 = $76 to produce.

From this, we can calculate that profit per surfboard is $200 - $76 = $124.

There is a 20% chance that Surfside will lose profits on 25,000 - 20,000 = 5,000 surfboards. Therefore, the expected value of lost profits = 20% * 5,000 surfboards * $124 profit per surfboard = $124K.

If the insurance was priced at $124K, the fair value, then the insurance company would not make any expected profit from offering this insurance. We can calculate what the insurance price needs to be in order for the insurance company to have a 10% profit margin.

Profit margin = (Price - Cost) / Price
10% = (P - $124K) / P
0.9P = $124K
P = $138K (rounded)

We expect insurance to cost $138K.

<u>Conclusion</u>: There is no summary or recommendation needed for this case.

Practice Case #10 – Polystore

Difficulty: Medium

Polystore is a national retail chain that sells a variety of different clothing brands for men, women, and children. They are one of four major clothing retail chains.

Five years ago, they introduced a loyalty program. Customers that sign up for the program receive a free loyalty card. This card is not a credit card. Customers can scan this card when making purchases at any Polystore location to earn 10 points for every $1 spent. After earning 1,000 points, customers can redeem these points for $5 off their next purchase.

The Chief Marketing Officer (CMO) of Polystore wants to assess how this program is doing and what Polystore can do to improve it.

(Sample framework is on the following page)

<u>Sample Framework</u>: One potential framework could look like the following. The candidate does not need to have this exact framework, but should capture many of these points.

- Profitability of loyalty card program
    - What are all of the costs associated with this program?
    - How much additional revenue has this program generated?
    - Is the program profitable?

- Customer awareness and usage
    - What percentage of customers are aware of this program?
    - What percentage of customers have signed up for this program?
    - Of those that signed up, what is the usage rate of their loyalty card?

- Competitor benchmarking
    - Do competitors also have a loyalty card program or something similar?
    - How are competitors' loyalty programs performing?
    - Can we leverage any best practices from competitors?

- Strategic alternatives
    - Are there other strategies or programs that can increase customer loyalty or engagement?
    - Do these other alternatives have a higher return on investment?

<u>Question 1</u>: We have collected some data from the CMO of Polystore. Based on the chart below, what is your assessment of the loyalty card program?

(Sample answer is on the following page)

<u>Answer to Question 1</u>: There are a few key takeaways from this chart.

One, we see that the loyalty card program accounts for a small percentage of total transactions and total spend. Although this chart does not show how many customers are in the loyalty card program, this chart implies that the penetration of the program is low, especially considering that this program was launched five years ago. There could be opportunities to improve marketing the program so that more customers participate.

Two, we see that although loyalty customers account for 20% of transactions, they account for 25% of total spend. This may suggest that the loyalty card is encouraging customers to purchase more each time they shop. However, it is also possible that customers that purchase more each time they shop are more likely to join the loyalty program. Without additional data, it is difficult to determine what is causing this.

Question 2: If the total number of transactions last year is 4M and the total spend is $160M, what is the spend per transaction for loyalty customers and non-loyalty customers?

(Sample answer is on the following page)

Answer to Question 2: We can calculate the average spend for each customer segment by dividing each segment's spending by the number of transactions.

$160M spend * 25% = $40M spend by loyalty
$160M spend * 75% = $120M spend by non-loyalty

4M transactions * 20% = 800K transactions by loyalty
4M transactions * 80% = 3.2M transactions by non-loyalty

Loyalty average spend = $40M / 800K = $50 per transaction
Non-loyalty average spend = $120M / 3.2M = $37.5 per transaction

Loyalty customers spend on average $50 per transaction compared to $37.5 per transaction among non-loyalty customers. Loyalty customers spend roughly 33% more per transaction. However, we do not know whether this is driven by the loyalty card or driven by the fact that customers that sign up for a loyalty card already spend more per transaction, on average.

Question 3: Before launching the loyalty program, Polystore polled their customers to ask if they would be likely to sign up for the program. They then segmented these customers as either "likely to sign up" or "unlikely to sign up." Based on the chart below, what is your assessment of the loyalty card program?

(Sample answer is on the following page)

Answer to Question 3: The key takeaway from this chart is that the customers that are likely to join the loyalty program already have a higher spend per transaction than those that are unlikely to join the program.

Let's calculate how much higher the average spend is for customers that are likely to sign up for the loyalty program versus customers that are unlikely to sign up.

($48 - $38) / $38M = 26% higher spend per transaction (rounded)

Recall from the previous problem that loyalty customers spend 33% more per transaction than non-loyalty customers. Therefore, the loyalty program likely only increases spend per transaction by roughly 33% - 26% = 7%.

While we do see loyalty customers having a higher spend per transaction than non-loyalty customers, a large proportion of this is caused by the fact that loyalty customers would already have a higher spend per transaction even if the loyalty program did not exist. Accounting for this, we estimate that the loyalty card increases average spend per transaction by 7%.

Question 4: We conducted customer interviews and pulled together the following information. What does this chart tell you?

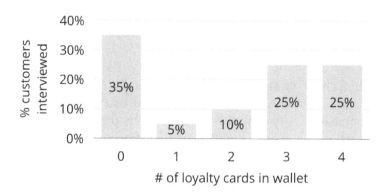

(Sample answer is on the following page)

Answer to Question 4: The key takeaway is that customers tend to have either no loyalty cards or many loyalty cards. Since 50% of customers have 3 or 4 different loyalty cards in their wallet, this suggests that loyalty cards may not actually promote loyalty. Customers will carry each loyalty card for each retail store they go to.

While this chart suggests that loyalty cards may not determine where a customer will shop, a loyalty card could affect how much they purchase in a given store. Recall from the previous problem that we estimated that a loyalty card increases average spend per transaction by about 7% for Polystore.

A secondary takeaway is that 35% of customers do not have a loyalty card. There could be an opportunity to target this segment to get them to sign up for a Polystore loyalty card, which should incentivize them to spend more per visit.

Conclusion: The CMO is eager to hear what you have to say about how Polystore's loyalty card program is doing and what ideas you have on how they can improve the program. What do you say?

(Sample conclusion is on the following page)

<u>Conclusion</u>: One potential recommendation is presented below.

"While Polystore's loyalty card program may not determine where customers shop, it does increase the average spend per transaction by about 7%. Therefore, the program should be continued and improved. There are two main areas of improvement.

One, we can improve marketing efforts to increase the number of customers that have Polystore's loyalty card. 35% of customers do not have any loyalty card from any of the national retailers.

Two, we could provide additional incentivizes to steer customers towards purchasing higher margin items. For example, we could give double or triple points for purchasing higher margin items.

For next steps, I'd like to look into two areas. One, look into the costs of the program to verify that the program is profitable. Two, look into competitor loyalty programs to see if there are any best practices Polystore can leverage."

Practice Case #11 – Bushel Co.

Difficulty: Hard

Bushel Co. is a high-quality backpack manufacturer that makes and sells all of their backpacks in the US. Several new players have recently entered the market and are applying competitive pressures. In addition, the costs of labor have been increasing over the past few years.

For these two reasons, Bushel Co. is considering producing some or all of their backpacks abroad in Vietnam. What factors should they consider when deciding whether to outsource their production to Vietnam?

(Sample framework is on the following page)

Sample Framework: One potential framework could look like the following. The candidate does not need to have this exact framework, but should capture many of these points.

- Financial implications
  - o How much cheaper is production in Vietnam?
  - o How much more will tariffs or transportation costs be?

- Production capabilities in Vietnam
  - o Can factories in Vietnam produce high-quality backpacks?
  - o Can factories in Vietnam deliver their products on-time?

- Customer needs and preferences
  - o How will customers react to outsourcing?
  - o Do customers have a strong preference for made-in-the-US products?

- Competitor benchmarking
  - o Do competitors outsource their production?
  - o What countries do competitors outsource to?

Question 1: Based on the following table, how much higher are profits for backpacks made in Vietnam vs. backpacks made in the US? Assume that when a backpack is produced at low-quality, it must be reproduced again, incurring the costs of: cost of goods sold, labor, transportation, and export tariffs again.

	Backpack made in the US	Backpack made in Vietnam
Backpack Retail Price	$100	$100
Cost of Goods Sold	$35	$20
Labor	$25	$5
Fixed Costs	$10	$10
Transportation	-	$10
Production Quality	1 in 20 are low-quality	1 in 5 are low-quality
Export Tariffs	-	$5

(Sample answer is on the following page)

<u>Answer to Question 1</u>: We will first calculate the cost to reproduce a low-quality backpack in the US. We can then take this figure and calculate the profit per backpack made in the US. If we repeat this set of calculations for backpacks made in Vietnam, we can compare the overall profit per backpack made in the US versus Vietnam.

Cost to reproduce low-quality backpack in the US = $35 + $25 = $60

Profit per backpack made in US = $100 - $35 - $25 - $10 - (1/20 * $60) = $27

Cost to reproduce low-quality backpack in Vietnam = $20 + $5 + $10 + $5 = $40

Profit per backpack made in Vietnam = $100 - $20 - $5 - $10 - $10 - $5 - (1/5 * $40) = $42

Therefore, profit per backpack is $15 higher if made in Vietnam than if made in the US. From a cost perspective, outsourcing is better.

Question 2: Bushel Co. believes that if they produce all of their backpacks in Vietnam, they will lose a segment of customers that love Bushel Co. for their made-in-the-US brand image. They estimate that they could lose up to 35% of their customers. Does it still make sense to outsource?

(Sample answer is on the following page)

<u>Answer to Question 2</u>: Recall that profit per backpack made in the US is $27. In Vietnam, it is $42. Let "x" be the number of customers.

Total profit if made in US = $27 * x = $27x

Total profit if made in Vietnam = $42 * (x − 0.35x) = $27.3x

We can then calculate the change in profit if we move production from the US to Vietnam.

Change in profit = ($27.3x − $27x) / $27x = **1.11%** increase in profits

Outsourcing to Vietnam still results in ~1% higher profits. However, the incremental profit is small and may not justify the risks of outsourcing.

<u>Question 3</u>: Another consideration for Bushel Co. is that the lead time for products produced in Vietnam is 6 months. The lead time for products produced in the US is just 1 month. Lead time is the time between when an order is placed and when an order is delivered. What are the potential downsides or risks of a longer lead time?

(Sample answer is on the following page)

<u>Answer to Question 3</u>: We can think about downsides as both economic downsides and non-economic downsides.

- Economic downsides
    - Higher working capital costs
    - Potentially higher likelihood for lost products

- Non-economic downsides
    - Requires forecasting customer demand at least 6 months in advance
    - Slower reactivity to swings in customer demand
    - Slower reactivity to production defects

Economic downsides may include higher working capital costs since cash will be tied up in inventory that takes six months to be delivered. Economic downsides also include potentially higher likelihood for lost products since these backpacks are in production and transit for so long.

Non-economic downsides include that Bushel Co. will need to forecast customer demand at least 6 months in advance since lead times are 6 months. Additionally, Bushel Co. will have slower reactivity to swings in customer demand. If customer demand is too high or too low, it will be difficult to adjust production levels quickly. Finally, Bushel Co. will also have slower reactivity to production defects. If a product is produced with a defect, Bushel Co. won't know until 6 months later when the product arrives.

Question 4: Another consideration for Bushel Co. is that if they were to outsource to Vietnam, their partner factory in Vietnam would require a minimum order size. Bushel Co. will place orders monthly, at the beginning of each month. The factory in Vietnam requires a minimum order size of 1,000 backpacks, which is higher than the average monthly customer demand of 600 backpacks. Therefore, Bushel Co. will likely incur holding or storage costs for unsold backpacks, which costs $1 per backpack per month.

- There is a 25% likelihood Bushel Co. will have 300 leftover backpacks; 200 will be stored for 1 month and 100 will be stored for 2 months before being sold

- There is a 50% likelihood Bushel Co. will have 400 leftover backpacks; 200 will be stored for 1 month, 100 will be stored for 2 months, and 100 will be stored for 3 months before being sold

- There is a 25% likelihood Bushel Co. will have 500 leftover backpacks; 200 will be stored for 1 month, 100 will be stored for 2 months, 100 will be stored for 3 months, and 100 will be stored for 4 months before being sold

What are average holdings costs per backpack ordered if Bushel Co. decides to outsource? Assuming that backpacks produced in the US have no holding costs, how does this affect profits?

(Sample answer is on the following page)

<u>Answer to Question 4</u>: Let's first calculate average holding costs, which is just a weighted average of the probabilities of each scenario and their respective total holding costs.

Holding costs of 300 leftover backpacks = ($1 * 200) + ($2 * 100) = $400

Holding costs of 400 leftover backpacks = ($1 * 200) + ($2 * 100) + ($3 * 100) = $700

Holding costs of 500 leftover backpacks = ($1 * 200) + ($2 * 100) + ($3 * 100) + ($4 * 100) = $1,100

Average holding costs = (25% * $400) + (50% * $700) + (25% * $1,100) = $725

We know that we'll be ordering 1,000 backpacks each time. Therefore, we can divide the average holding costs by the number of backpacks ordered to get average holding cost per backpack ordered.

Average holding cost / backpack ordered = $725 / 1000 backpacks = **$0.725**

Therefore, the average holding cost per backpack ordered is **$0.725**.

Next, we'll look at how this additional holding cost for outsourced production impacts profits. Recall that profit per backpack made in the US is $27 and profit per backpack made in Vietnam is $42. Also recall that if Bushel Co. outsources, they would lose 35% of customers. There are no holding costs if backpacks are made in the US, but an average holding cost of $0.725 per backpack if made in Vietnam.

Letting "x" be the number of customers, we can write expressions for total profit.

Total profit of backpacks made in US = $27 * x = $27x

Total profit of backpacks made in Vietnam = ($42 - $0.725) * (x – 0.35x) = $26.8x (rounded)

Change in profit = ($26.8x - $27x) / $27x = **-0.6%**

Therefore, once we take into account holding costs, it no longer makes sense to outsource to Vietnam. Costs would be higher and profits would decrease by 0.6%.

<u>Conclusion</u>: The CEO of Bushel Co. asks you for a summary of your recommendation. Should they outsource the production of their backpacks to Vietnam?

(Sample conclusion is on the following page)

<u>Sample Conclusion</u>: One potential recommendation is presented below.

"I recommend that Bushel Co. does not outsource to Vietnam. There are two reasons to support this.

One, outsourcing to Vietnam would actually decrease overall profits. Although production costs are lower in Vietnam, the combination of increased holding costs and a loss of customers as a result of outsourcing means lower overall profits. Bushel Co. profits would actually decrease by 0.6% if they decided to outsource.

Two, lead times in Vietnam are significantly longer, at 6 months compared to 1 month in the US. This results in downsides such as higher working capital costs and slower reactivity to changes in customer demand or identification of production errors.

For next steps, I'd like to look into two areas. One, look into other potential countries that may have lower outsourcing costs. Two, look into whether competitors are outsourcing to benchmark our production strategy compared to theirs."

Practice Case #12 - Prytown

Difficulty: Medium

Prytown is a fictitious city that is in dire need of cash. They are looking for a buyer to purchase the rights to their city's parking meters. For an upfront lump sum, the buyer would own all of Prytown's parking meters and collect all revenues generated from them.

Greyrock is a private equity firm that is considering making this investment. They have hired us to: (1) help them determine if they should make this investment and (2) determine how much they should bid for the rights to Prytown's parking meters.

(Sample framework is on the following page)

<u>Sample Framework</u>: One potential framework could look like the following. The candidate does not need to have this exact framework, but should capture many of these points.

- Parking meter market attractiveness
    - What is the size of the parking meter market in Prytown?
    - What is the growth rate of this market?
    - What are average profit margins in this market?

- Greyrock's capabilities
    - Does Greyrock know how to manage parking meters?
    - Are there any synergies Greyrock can realize with their existing portfolio of companies?

- Expected profitability
    - What are the expected revenues?
    - What are the expected costs?

- Purchasing price
    - What return on investment is Greyrock targeting?
    - What purchase price is required to achieve this target?

<u>Question 1</u>: What is the market size of parking meters in Prytown? Assume that Prytown is a city of roughly 3M people and that an hour of parking at a metered parking spot is $2. Make all other assumptions.

(Sample answer is on the following page)

<u>Answer to Question 1</u>: One potential structure for this market sizing problem could look like the following:

- Start with Prytown's population of 3M people

- Estimate the average household size

- Estimate the average number of cars per household

- Assume 1 car = 1 parking spot needed

- Estimate the percentage of parking spots that are metered

- Estimate the number of hours per year that meters operate

- Estimate the percentage of time that metered parking spots are occupied

- Multiply by the hourly metered parking spot rate of $2 per hour

Prytown has 3M people. Assume that the average household size is 3 people. Therefore, there are 3M / 3 = 1M households.

Assume an average of 0.5 cars per household, giving us 1M * 0.5 = 500K cars.

500K cars imply 500K parking spots needed.

Assume that 10% of parking spots are metered, giving us 500K * 10% = 50K metered parking spots.

Assuming that parking meters operate 365 days and 24 hours a day, there are 365 * 24 = 8,760 hours of parking per meter.

Assuming parking spots are occupied 20% of the time, 8,760 * 20% = 1,752 hours of paid parking per meter.

With an hourly rate of $2 per hour, 1,752 * $2 = $3,504 generated per parking meter. Let's round this number to $3,500.

Finally, 50K meters * $3,500 per meter per year = **$175M**.

Therefore, we estimate that the market size of parking meters in Prytown is $175M.

<u>Question 2</u>: If Greyrock were to purchase the rights to Prytown's parking meters, what are the potential costs that Greyrock might incur in order to manage and operate their parking meters?

(Sample answer is on the following page)

<u>Answer to Question 2</u>: One potential answer could be structured as listing one-time costs and recurring costs.

- One-time costs
  - Purchase price of the rights to Prytown's parking meters
  - Initial replacement costs of broken parking meters

- Recurring costs
  - Annual maintenance and repair of parking meters
  - Annual salaries of parking meter officers

Question 3: Greyrock wants to generate a 10% return on investment within 10 years. Assuming the following information, what is the maximum price they should bid for the rights to Prytown's parking meters?

- Assume that in the first question, you determined Prytown has 50,000 parking meters and annual revenue is $175M per year

- Upon purchase, 20% of these parking meters need to be replaced at a cost of $20,000 per parking meter

- Maintenance costs are $200 per parking meter per month

- Greyrock will need to hire one parking officer for every 125 parking meters

- Parking officers work 40 hours a week, 50 weeks a year, at a wage of $25 per hour

(Sample answer is on the following page)

<u>Answer to Question 3</u>: We'll first calculate one-time costs.

50,000 meters * 20% replaced * $20,000 replacement cost = $200M replacement costs

Next, we'll calculate recurring costs.

50,000 meters * 12 months * $200 per month in maintenance = $120M annual maintenance costs

50,000 / 125 = 400 employees needed

400 employees * 40 hours per week * 50 weeks per year * $25 per hour = $20M annual labor costs

Annual profit = $175M - $120M - $20M = $35M

10-year profit, excluding one-time costs = 10 * $35M = $350M

10-year profit, including one-time costs = $350M - $200M = $150M

Now that we know what 10-year profits will be once we've accounted for all costs, we can calculate the maximum price Greyrock should bid in order to generate a 10% return on investment.

Return on investment = (Profit – Investment) / Investment
10% = ($150M – Investment) / Investment
Investment = $136.4M

Greyrock should bid no more than $136.4M in order to achieve a 10% return on investment after 10 years.

<u>Question 4</u>: What are some ways that Greyrock could further increase revenues from their parking meters?

(Sample answer is on the following page)

<u>Answer to Question 4</u>: We can think about ways to increase revenues as pricing-related strategies and non-pricing-related strategies.

- Pricing-related strategies
  - Increase meter fare during high parking demand hours
  - Offer discounted rates during low parking demand hours
  - Offer monthly or annual parking rates

- Non-pricing-related strategies
  - Rent out parking spaces for other uses (e.g., street vendors, car rental companies)
  - Increase accessibility of parking spots (e.g., an app to check for availability)
  - Move parking meters to higher demand areas

<u>Conclusion</u>: Should Greyrock purchase the rights to Prytown's parking meters? If so, how much should they bid?

(Sample conclusion is on the following page)

<u>Sample Conclusion</u>: One potential recommendation is presented below.

"I recommend Greyrock place a bid of no more than $136.4M for Prytown's parking meters. There are three reasons to support this.

One, parking meters are a profitable business. Annual expected profits for Prytown's parking meters are $35M per year.

Two, a bid of no more than $136.4M ensures that Greyrock will achieve at least a 10% return on investment after 10 years.

Three, there may be additional opportunities to further increase revenues by changing pricing strategies or by renting empty parking space to street vendors or car rental companies.

For next steps, I'd like to look into two areas. One, check that Greyrock has the capability to manage and operate parking meters well. Two, look into what strategies Greyrock should pursue to further increase revenues."

Practice Case #13 - Telcast

Difficulty: Medium

Telcast provides satellite TV service nationwide in the US. In recent years, their customer base is being threatened by other telecommunications and cable companies that are offering a combined package of TV, internet, and home phone service. Our client is considering deploying a wireless network of base stations to offer high-speed, broadband internet. Should Telcast go into the broadband internet space?

(Sample framework is on the following page)

<u>Sample Framework</u>: One potential framework could look like the following. The candidate does not need to have this exact framework, but should capture many of these points.

- Internet market attractiveness
  - What is the market size?
  - What is the market growth rate?
  - What are the average profit margins?

- Telcast's capabilities
  - Does Telcast have the capital needed?
  - Do they have the capability to deploy and maintain base stations?
  - Do they have distribution channels to sell internet subscriptions?

- Potential synergies
  - How much would Telcast be able to cross-sell to existing customers?
  - Would Telcast get access to new customer segments?
  - Are there potential cost synergies?

- Expected profitability
  - What are the expected revenues?
  - What are the expected costs?
  - How long will it take Telcast to break even on this investment?

<u>Question 1</u>: What are all of the potential costs of offering high-speed, broadband internet?

(Sample answer is on the following page)

<u>Answer to Question 1</u>: We can think about costs as either one-time costs or recurring costs.

- One-time costs
    - Installation of base stations
    - Licenses needed to install base stations
    - Additional equipment (e.g., wires, customer premise equipment)

- Recurring costs
    - Maintenance costs of the base stations
    - Leases for the base station land
    - Sales and marketing costs
    - Customer service costs

Question 2: How many base stations does Telcast need to provide internet to all of their potential customers in the US? Assume the following:

- Telcast expects to capture 5% market share for broadband internet

- A base station has a bandwidth of 80,000 kbps

- Each household requires an average of 320 kbps

- No more than 50% of users are online at any point in time

(Sample answer is on the following page)

<u>Answer to Question 2</u>: One potential structure for this estimation question could look like the following:

- Start with the US population

- Estimate the number of people per household

- Multiply by Telcast's expected market share to get the number of households serviced

- Multiply by the required kbps per household

- Multiply by the percentage of users that are online at any point in time

- Divide by the bandwidth, in kbps, per base station

Assume that the US population is 320M people and that there is an average of 2.5 people per household. From this, we get 320M / 2.5 = 128M households.

With 5% market share, we would service 128M * 5% = 6.4M households.

Each household requires 320 kbps, so we need to deliver a total of 6.4M households * 320 kbps = 2,048M kbps.

However, since no more than 50% of users are online at any point in time, we actually need to deliver only 2,048M kbps * 50% = 1,024M kbps.

Each base station has a bandwidth of 80,000 kbps, so we need 1,024M kbps / 80,000 kbps per base station = 12,800 base station.

Therefore, Telcast needs to deploy 12,800 base stations.

<u>Question 3</u>: Telcast is considering whether to build their own base stations or to lease them for a rental and maintenance fee. Which do you recommend Telcast to do?

(Sample answer is on the following page)

<u>Answer to Question 3</u>: Let's consider the advantages and disadvantages of the build versus lease options.

Build:

- + Full control over network deployment and service levels

- – High initial investment

- – Slower market entry

Lease:

- + Smaller initial investment

- + Faster market entry

- – Likely more expensive in the long-run

- – Existing towers may not service or cover all of Telcast's customers

Taking all of these considerations into account, we might recommend that Telcast should lease base stations for faster market entry and lower initial costs.

Question 4: Telcast decides to lease their base stations at a cost of $100K per base station per year. Additional costs are annual licensing costs (shown below) and customer premise equipment (CPE). CPE costs $200 per household and Telcast believes they can pass 50% of the costs to the customer. Assume that Telcast needs 12,800 base stations, there are 6.4M households that Telcast would service, and that each household pays $20 per month for internet.

What is Telcast's expected annual profitability?

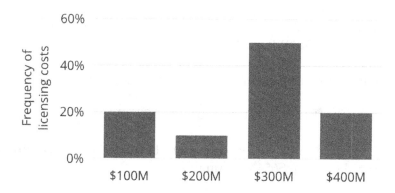

(Sample answer is on the following page)

<u>Answer to Question 4</u>: Let's calculate revenues first.

Revenue = 6.4M households * $20 per month * 12 months per year = $1.536B

Next, let's calculate the different costs.

Base station costs = 12,800 base stations * $100,000 = $1.28B

CPE costs = 6.4M households * $200 * (1 – 50%) = $640M

Annual license costs = (20% * $100M) + (10% * $200M) + (50% * $300M) + (20% * $400M) = $270M

Subtracting costs from revenues, we can calculate annual profit.

Annual profit = $1.536B - $1.28B - $640M - $270M = -$654M

Telcast should not offer internet because they would be unprofitable, losing $654M annually.

Question 5: If Telcast cannot compete with competitors by offering high-speed, broadband internet, what other strategies can they pursue in order to grow profits?

(Sample answer is on the following page)

<u>Answer to Question 5</u>: We can think about potential strategies as either core business strategies or adjacent business strategies.

- Core business strategies
    - o Acquire a satellite TV competitor to increase scale, decreasing costs
    - o Segment their customers and focus on growing the most profitable segment
    - o Focus on technology innovations to improve their network capabilities or offerings

- Adjacent business strategies
    - o Acquire a high-speed, broadband internet player
    - o Consider entering the home phone services market organically or through acquisition
    - o Look into entering the TV content market to differentiate their content

<u>Conclusion</u>: There is no summary or recommendation needed for this case.

Practice Case #14 – Burger Corp

Difficulty: Medium

Burger Corp is the third largest fast food restaurant chain in the US, specializing in making great-tasting beef burgers. As part of their growth strategy, Burger Corp is considering acquiring Good Chicken Eats, another fast food chain that specializes in chicken sandwiches, chicken nuggets, and chicken tenders.

The corporate development team of Burger Corp has hired you to advise them on whether they should acquire Good Chicken Eats.

(Sample framework is on the following page)

<u>Sample Framework</u>: One potential framework could look like the following. The candidate does not need to have this exact framework, but should capture many of these points.

- Fast food chicken market attractiveness
    - How large is the fast food chicken market?
    - What is the market growth rate?
    - What are the average profit margins?

- Good Chicken Eats attractiveness
    - Is Good Chicken Eats profitable?
    - What is their market positioning?
    - Do they have any competitive advantages or differentiation?

- Acquisition synergies
    - Are there any revenue synergies that can be realized?
    - Are there any cost synergies that can be realized?

- Acquisition financials
    - Is the acquisition price fair?
    - How long will it take Burger Corp to break even on this acquisition?

Question 1: The corporate development team at Burger Corp is thinking about what potential synergies can be realized from this acquisition. What are some potential synergies you can think of? Here are some facts.

# of Locations	Burger Corp	Good Chicken Eats
North America	2,900	1,000
Europe	1,400	0
Asia	1,200	0
Other	500	0
Total	6,000	1,000

Financial metrics	Burger Corp	Good Chicken Eats
Annual revenue	$6B	$750M
Cost of sales	40% of revenue	30% of revenue
Operating costs	25% of revenue	25% of revenue
Property & equipment	5% of revenue	10% of revenue
General & administrative	5% of revenue	5% of revenue

(Sample answer is on the following page)

<u>Answer to Question 1</u>: We can think about synergies as either revenue synergies or cost synergies.

- Revenue synergies
    - Burger Corp could cross-sell chicken-related items in their restaurants
    - Burger Corp has an international presence, which could help Good Chicken Eats expand internationally
    - Burger Corp has higher revenue per store and could help Good Chicken Eats improve this metric

- Cost synergies
    - General & administrative costs could be consolidated
    - Larger scale would lower cost of sales due to higher purchasing power
    - Burger Corp has lower property & equipment costs and could help Good Chicken Eats improve on this

<u>Question 2</u>: The corporate development team thinks that through synergies, they can double Good Chicken Eats' market share in the US over the next 10 years. A capital infusion would help Good Chicken Eats' triple their number of stores. What level of sales per store does Good Chicken Eats need to achieve this? Assume that annual fast food chicken consumption per person in the US is $10 today, but will increase to $20 in 10 years. You can also assume that the US population is 300M people.

(Sample answer is on the following page)

<u>Answer to Question 2</u>: Recall that Good Chicken Eats' revenue is $750M and that they have 1,000 locations.

The fast food chicken market size today = 300M people * $10 = $3B.

Good Chicken Eats' market share = $750M / $3B = 25% market share.

The fast food chicken market size in 10 years = 300M people * $20 = $6B.

If Good Chicken Eats doubles their market share and triples the number of locations, then average sales per store = ($6B * 50%) / (3 * 1,000) = $1M per store.

Good Chicken Eats needs $1M of revenue per store, which seems plausible. This is a ~33% increase and the market is expected to double in size.

<u>Question 3</u>: Another synergy idea is to increase Burger Corp's profits by selling chicken sandwiches, chicken nuggets, and chicken tenders in their restaurants. How would you assess the impact of this move on Burger Corp's profits?

(Sample answer is on the following page)

<u>Answer to Question 3</u>: We can think about the implications for Burger Corp's profits in terms of revenue considerations and cost considerations.

- Revenue considerations
    - o How much revenue would Burger Corp generate from selling these items?
    - o Will offering these items cannibalize existing sales of beef burgers?

- Cost considerations
    - o What are the costs of these fast food chicken items?
    - o Are there additional costs for marketing the new items or training the staff?
    - o Are there additional costs for new equipment or extra restaurant space?

We can formulate an equation to measure the change in profits. At a high-level, the change in profits is equal to the number of chicken items sold times the difference between their prices and variable costs, minus any additional fixed costs, minus cannibalized sales profits of beef burgers.

Change in Profits = Quantity Chicken Items Sold * (Price - Variable Costs) - Additional Fixed Costs - Cannibalized Sales Profits

Question 4: What is the incremental profit per restaurant if Burger Corp sells chicken items in their restaurants? Here is some additional information:

- The average Burger Corp restaurant sells 200,000 burgers each year at $5 each with a variable cost of $2

- Offering chicken items would increase annual fixed costs in each Burger Corp restaurant by $100K

- Each Burger Corp restaurant expects to sell 50,000 chicken sandwiches at $5 each ($3 variable cost), 20,000 chicken nuggets at $4 each ($1 variable cost), and 20,000 chicken tenders at $6 each ($2 variable cost)

- The cannibalization rates for Burger Corp's burger sales are 10% for chicken sandwiches, 5% for chicken nuggets, and 5% for chicken tenders. Cannibalization rate is defined as the percentage of Burger Corp's burgers that will not be sold because they have been replaced with chicken item sales

(Sample answer is on the following page)

<u>Answer to Question 4</u>: Let's start by calculating the original profit per restaurant. If each restaurant sells 200K burgers at a price of $5 and a variable cost of $2, then profit = 200K * $3 = $600K.

We can then calculate the new profit from selling chicken sandwiches, chicken nuggets, and chicken tenders using the same profit formula.

Profit from chicken sandwiches = 50K * ($5 - $3) = $100K
Profit from chicken nuggets = 20K * ($4 - $1) = $60K
Profit from chicken tenders = 20K * ($6 - $2) = $80K

We'll then need to calculate the lost burger sales profit due to cannibalization. Some customers that would have previously purchased beef burgers will purchase them no longer because they are purchasing one of the new chicken items. The cannibalized profit is calculated by taking the original profit from selling burgers, which is $600K, times the sum of all of the cannibalization rates.

Loss in profit from cannibalization = 600K * (10% + 5% + 5%) = $120K

Finally, we'll need to take into account increased annual fixed costs.

Loss in profit from increased fixed costs = $100K

We can now calculate what new profit per restaurant will be.

New profit = $600K + $100K + $60K + $80K - $120K - $100K = $620K

Profit per restaurant will increase by $20K, from $600K to $620K.

<u>Conclusion</u>: You are asked to present a summary of your findings and recommendations to the corporate development team at Burger Corp. What do you say?

(Sample conclusion is on the following page)

<u>Sample Conclusion</u>: One potential recommendation is presented below.

"I recommend that Burger Corp acquire Good Chicken Eats. There are three reasons that support this.

One, there are significant synergies to be realized. On the revenue-side, Burger Corp could help Good Chicken Eats expand internationally and increase sales per store. On the cost-side, Burger Corp could consolidate general and administrative costs and lower cost of sales due to higher purchasing power from increased scale.

Two, a capital infusion from Burger Corp could help Good Chicken Eats triple their number of stores and double their market share over the next 10 years. This seems feasible because each store would only need to grow sales by ~33% over this time period while the market is doubling in size.

Three, by cross-selling chicken fast food items in Burger Corp's existing restaurants, they can increase profits by $20K annually in each store. With 6,000 stores, annual profits would increase by $120M.

For next steps, I'd like to look into two areas. One, assess whether Burger Corp and Good Chicken Eats are compatible companies that can be integrated smoothly. Two, assess whether the acquisition price is reasonable and fair."

Practice Case #15 – Pink Cross

Difficulty: Hard

Pink Cross is a health care company that services the west coast of the US. They both insure patients and provide health care services. Patients pay a fixed premium to Pink Cross each month and Pink Cross covers all necessary health services, ranging from physician primary care to hospitalizations.

Pink Cross has 500,000 patients enrolled in their insurance plan and has 500 salaried physicians that represent a wide range of specialty areas, such as cardiology or neurology. When a patient needs medical treatment in a specialty area not covered by a Pink Cross physician, they are referred outside of the Pink Cross network for care and Pink Cross pays for the referral costs and service.

Pink Cross has been seeing a decline in profitability over the past few years. How can they improve their financial situation?

(Sample framework is on the following page)

<u>Sample Framework</u>: One potential framework could look like the following. The candidate does not need to have this exact framework, but should capture many of these points.

- Pink Cross profitability drivers
    - o Have revenues gone down?
        - ▪ Have the number of patients decreased?
        - ▪ Have premiums decreased?
    - o Have costs gone up?
        - ▪ Have variable costs increased?
        - ▪ Have fixed costs increased?

- Patient needs and preferences
    - o Have patient needs changed?
    - o Have patient behaviors changed?
    - o Has the mix of patients changed?

- Competitor benchmarking
    - o Are competitors also seeing a decline in profitability?
    - o Have competitors made any recent strategic moves?

- Health care market trends
    - o Are there new technologies impacting health care?
    - o Are there new regulations impacting health care?

<u>Question 1</u>: You perform some competitor benchmarking with another health care insurance provider and find the following information. What are some potential reasons why Pink Cross' average cost per referral is higher than Johnson Health?

	# of patients	Average cost per referral
Pink Cross	500,000	$25
Johnson Health	700,000	$20

(Sample answer is on the following page)

<u>Answer to Question 1</u>: We can think about potential reasons by looking at reasons on the physician-side, patient-side, and company-side.

- Physician reasons
    - Pink Cross' physicians might be referring patients to physicians that have higher than average service costs
    - Pink Cross' mix of physician specialties could require referrals to other specialties that are more expensive

- Patient reasons
    - Pink Cross has a higher proportion of patients that are sicker or older, making them more expensive to treat when referred
    - Patients are asking for referrals to more expensive physicians

- Company reasons
    - Pink Cross does not have the scale that Johnson Health has to negotiate lower referral costs
    - Pink Cross' referral guidelines send patients to more expensive physicians

Question 2: The Chief Health Officer of Pink Cross believes that they may be paying too much in neurology referral costs for their patients. Pink Cross currently pays for 150,000 neurology referrals annually. What is the expected number of neurology referrals each year?

- 25% of Pink Cross' patients are over the age of 65

- Patients with neurological conditions visit neurologists an average of 3 times per year through referrals while those with serious neurological conditions visit 5 times per year through referrals

- In the US, the prevalence of neurological conditions for people under the age of 65 is 2%, which increases to 20% for those over the age of 65

- In the US, 25% of neurological conditions are considered serious

(Sample answer is on the following page)

<u>Answer to Question 2</u>: We'll first calculate the number of patients over the age of 65.

500,000 patients * 25% = 125,000 patients that are over the age of 65. This also means that 375,000 patients are under the age of 65.

We can then calculate the number of people with neurological conditions.

(20% * 125,000) + (2% * 375,000) = 32,500 patients with neurological conditions.

Next, we'll calculate how many people have serious neurological conditions versus non-serious conditions.

25% * 32,500 = 8,125 patients with serious neurological conditions. This also means that 24,375 patients have non-serious conditions.

Finally, we can calculate the expected number of referrals.

Expected number of referrals = (8,125 * 5) + (24,375 * 3) = 113,750 referrals.

Pink Cross should expect 113,750 referrals, but sees 150,000 referrals per year. This is ~30% higher than expected.

Question 3: What are the potential reasons why Pink Cross' number of neurology referrals is significantly higher than expected?

(Sample answer is on the following page)

<u>Answer to Question 3</u>: Again, we can structure our answer as physician reasons, patient reasons, and company reasons.

- Physician reasons
    - Pink Cross' physicians are not as experienced or comfortable treating patients, so tend to refer more frequently
    - Pink Cross' physician expertise doesn't satisfy patient demand, requiring more referrals

- Patient reasons
    - Patients are demanding referrals when they don't need one
    - Pink Cross' patients have a higher prevalence of neurological conditions

- Company reasons
    - Pink Cross does not provide clear guidelines on when to refer patients
    - There are no incentives or penalties to prevent physicians from referring patients who don't need referrals

<u>Question 4</u>: After some brainstorming, your team is considering launching an initiative in which they: (1) spend $2M more each year to pay primary care physicians to handle patients with acute neurological conditions, and (2) pay the top 20 physicians with the lowest referral rates $50,000 to incentivize physicians to keep referral rates low.

One potential complication is that Pink Cross may be sued if a patient who actually needs a referral does not get a referral because physicians are incentivized to keep referral rates low. Pink Cross estimates that 0.1% of the decrease in the number of referrals will result in a lawsuit. The average lawsuit settlement is $200,000.

What percentage reduction in neurology referrals does Pink Cross need to break even on this initiative? Assume the average cost of a neurology referral is $500.

(Sample answer is on the following page)

<u>Answer to Question 4</u>: Let's first calculate the initiative cost. This is the $2M in additional pay to primary care physicians plus the $50,000 bonus awarded to the top 20 physicians.

Initiative cost = $2M + (20 * $50K) = $3M

Let's calculate the lawsuit costs next. Let "x" be the decrease in the number of referrals.

Lawsuit costs = x * 0.1% * $200K = $200x

Therefore, total costs = $3M + $200x

The total savings from the initiative = x * $500 = $500x

We can now set total costs equal to total savings and solve for "x" in order to determine the decrease in referrals needed to break even.

$3M + 200x = 500x
300x = $3M
x = 10,000

This means that the number of referrals needs to decrease by 10,000 in order to break even on this initiative. We know that Pink Cross sees 150,000 neurology referrals a year, so we can calculate what percent reduction this is.

10,000 / 150,000 = 6.67%

A 6.67% reduction in referrals is needed to break even, which seems reasonable.

Question 5: The General Counsel for Pink Cross is unsure of the previous estimate that 0.1% of the decrease in the number of referrals will result in a lawsuit. What is the maximum possible percentage this estimate can be in order for Pink Cross to be able to break even on this investment?

(Sample answer is on the following page)

<u>Answer to Question 5</u>: Recall in the previous problem that we set total savings equal to total initiative costs in order to find the breakeven point, where "x" is the decrease in the number of referrals.

$3M + $200x = $500x

In this equation, the "$200x" portion represents the average cost of a lawsuit for each reduction in referrals.

If the average cost of a lawsuit per reduction in referrals increases to "$500x", it will be impossible for Pink Cross to break even. This is because the savings per reduction in referral is $500 while the lawsuit cost per reduction in referral is also $500. Therefore, Pink Cross would not be able to recoup the $3M initiative costs in these circumstances, making it impossible to break even.

If we let "r" be the lawsuit rate per reduction in referrals, we can solve for the lawsuit rate that would make it impossible to break even.

r * x * $200,000 = 500x
r = 0.25%

Therefore, we know that the lawsuit rate must be less than 0.25%.

Continuing further with this problem, we can actually calculate the exact maximum lawsuit rate if we take the extreme scenario that referrals are reduced from 150,000 to 0 as a result of this initiative.

If this were the case, we would get a total savings of 150,000 referrals * $500 = $75M.

Total lawsuit costs would be $200,000 * r * 150,000 referrals.

Setting total savings equal to total costs, we can solve for "r" to get the maximum lawsuit rate.

$75M = $3M + ($200K * r * 150,000)
r = 0.24%

Therefore, the highest lawsuit rate that Pink Cross could still break even on from this initiative is 0.24%.

<u>Question 6</u>: Your team decides to not launch the newly proposed initiative because they feel the margin of error for the lawsuit rate is quite high. The CEO appreciates the analysis you have done so far, but asks you what are the other ways Pink Cross could reduce the cost of their specialist referrals?

(Sample answer is on the following page)

<u>Answer to Question 6</u>: Again, we can think of ideas as physician strategies, patient strategies, and company strategies.

- Physician strategies
    o Provide physician training on how to treat acute neurological conditions
    o Provide incentives to physicians to treat patients themselves when appropriate

- Patient strategies
    o Educate patients on when they should seek a referral
    o Provide incentives to acute or stable patients to self-manage their conditions

- Company strategies
    o Enact a referral committee to approve or reject physician referrals
    o Try to screen out potential patients that have a higher likelihood of getting or having neurological conditions

<u>Conclusion</u>: There is no summary or recommendation needed for this case.

Final Thoughts

You've practiced answering all of the different types of questions you could get asked during a case interview. You've applied these learnings to solve real, full-length practice cases. You are well on your way towards mastering consulting case interviews.

Don't stop here. I recommend getting with your case interview partner and practicing as many cases as you have the time for. What separates a candidate that gets multiple consulting job offers from a candidate that doesn't receive any is ruthless, targeted practice.

Have a list of improvement or development areas for yourself based on your performance in previous practice cases. Each time you do a practice case interview, work on improving one or two of these development areas.

When you feel that you have reached a learning plateau and don't have any development areas remaining, find a former management consultant and ask if they would be willing to give you a mock interview. Their specific feedback and advice can be incredibly valuable. They'll often point out development areas that you would have otherwise not been able to identify.

Preparing for case interviews can take a significant amount of time, but if consulting is truly the job you want, then the time invested is worth it. Case interviews can actually be quite fun. You get to solve interesting business problems in under an hour. If you feel yourself enjoying doing practice cases, then that is a good sign that you will find consulting an enjoyable and fulfilling profession.

I wish you the best of luck!

Other case interview preparation resources

For those looking for a one-week crash course on consulting case interviews, use the online course at **HackingTheCaseInterview.com**.

The goal of the crash course is to help you pass your upcoming interview in the shortest amount of time possible. It is an all-inclusive course that contains (1) all of the strategies and knowledge you need to know, and (2) all of the practice problems and cases you need to do to quickly become a case interview expert.

Through this online crash course:

- Engage with 50+ concise video lessons that consolidate hundreds of hours of knowledge and experience into a 10-15 hour learning experience

- Learn advanced strategies to differentiate yourself from other candidates and become a top 1% interview candidate

- Hone your case interview skills through 15 additional challenging practice cases

Visit **HackingTheCaseInterview.com** to take your case interview skills to the next level.

About the Author

Taylor Warfield is a former Bain management consultant, case interviewer, and case workshop leader. His top-selling case interview prep book, "Hacking the Case Interview," has helped 3,000+ students in 13+ countries. His book, online course, and coaching have helped hundreds of candidates land job offers at top consulting firms such as McKinsey, BCG, and Bain. He is the founder of **HackingTheCaseInterview.com**

Made in the USA
Coppell, TX
14 August 2024

35978881R00174